J. A. Harrison, B.Sc., Ph.D.
Lecturer in Electrical Engineering and Electronics
University of Liverpool

An introduction to electric power systems

GW00569864

Longman
London and New York

To my wife, Mary

Longman Group Limited London

Associated companies, branches and representatives throughout the world

Published in the United States of America by Longman Inc., New York

© Longman Group Limited 1980

All rights reserved. No part of this publication may be reproduced, stored in a retrieval system, or transmitted in any form or by any means, electronic, mechanical, photocopying, recording, or otherwise, without the prior permission of the Copyright owner.

First published 1980

British Library Cataloguing in Publication Data

Harrison, J. A.
  An introduction to electric power systems.
  1. Electric power systems
  I. Title
621.31   TK1001   79-41201

  ISBN 0-582-30503-9

Printed in England by McCorquodale (Newton) Ltd., Newton-le-Willows, Lancas

Contents

Contents

Acknowledgements

We are indebted to the following for permission to reproduce copyright material:

BICC Ltd for extracts from *Oil-Filled Cable Systems* to compile our Table 4.3; Central Electricity Generating Board for information to compile our Table 4.1, and extracts from *C.E.G.B. Annual Reports and Accounts 1978–79* to compile our Table 7.1 and Fig. 7.1; Guinness Superlatives Ltd for a slightly adapted extract from *Guinness Book of Records*; Institution of Electrical Engineers and the authors, R. J. S. Ward and M. N. Eggleton for extracts from 'Electrical parameters of 400 kV and 275 kV Overhead lines used in England and Wales' in *IEE Conference Paper No 44* September 1968 to compile our Table 4.2.

Preface

This book is based on a short introductory course given to students in the Department of Electrical Engineering and Electronics at the University of Liverpool. Some of these students will later specialise in power systems, and for them the book is intended to lay a solid foundation on which their further studies can be built. For other students, this will be the sum total of their formal teaching in power systems, and for them the book will, I hope, provide a balanced view of the main features of electric power systems, together with some of the problems facing the power engineer. I have tried also to answer in the text a number of questions about power systems that puzzle many people who are not electrical engineers. For example: why do we have unsightly pylons in the countryside when electricity can be carried underground in cables? Why do the pylons have to be so large? What is the purpose of a pumped storage scheme? I have assumed that the reader will have a knowledge of single-phase electrical circuits: three-phase circuits are introduced in the text. The mathematics required is not very demanding: school sixth form standard would suffice.

Why another book on power systems? There are many very good, comprehensive and detailed textbooks covering the subject, but I have found, from talking to students, that many of them are unwilling to buy such books. This is because they go into the subject in far too much detail which can be bewildering to a student meeting the subject for the first time, and also because these books are relatively too expensive for a student who may only be taking the subject at an introductory level.

I hope you will find this book readable, easy to understand and perhaps stimulating so that you will go on to study power systems at a more advanced level.

I am grateful to the Central Electricity Generating Board for permission to reproduce the information in Table 7.1 and Fig. 7.1 and many other data, to the BICC Ltd for information on cables and to Mr Gray of Hatfield Polytechnic, for reading the manuscript and making many helpful suggestions. I am also grateful to my elder daughter, Sonja, who encouraged me to write this book.

Tony Harrison

List of symbols

SI units (Le Système International d'Unités)

A	ampere, the unit of current
F	farad, the unit of capacitance
H	henry, the unit of inductance
Hz	hertz, the unit of frequency, i.e. the number of cycles per second
J	joule, the unit of energy
m	metre, the unit of length
s	second, the unit of time
T	tesla, the unit of magnetic flux density
V	volt, the unit of potential difference and electromotive force
W	watt, the unit of power
Wb	weber, the unit of magnetic flux
Ω	ohm, the unit of resistance, reactance and impedance
rad	radian, the unit of plane angle.

SI prefixes

p	pico, 10^{-12}
n	nano, 10^{-9}
μ	micro, 10^{-6}
m	milli, 10^{-3}
c	centi, 10^{-2}
k	kilo, 10^{3}
M	mega, 10^{6}
G	giga, 10^{9}
T	tera, 10^{12}

Quantity symbols

A	area
B	magnetic flux density

List of symbols

C	capacitance
d	distance
d_{eq}	equivalent distance
E	root mean square value of the electromotive force
e	instantaneous value of the electromotive force
f	frequency in Hz
h	height
I	current
I_B	base value of the current
I_{pu}	per-unit value of the current
I_{sc}	short-circuit current
J	moment of inertia
j	square root of minus one
L	inductance
N	number of turns, or transformation ratio
P	real power
Q	reactive power
R	resistance
r	radius
S	apparent power
S_B	base value of the apparent power
S_{sc}	short-circuit apparent power
T	temperature
t	time
V	root mean square value of the potential difference (voltage)
V_B	base value of the voltage
V_L	line voltage
V_P	phase voltage
V_{pu}	per-unit value of the voltage
V_T	Thévenin equivalent phase voltage
v	instantaneous value of the voltage
X	reactance
X'	transient reactance
X_s	synchronous reactance
X_{pu}	per-unit value of the reactance
x	variable length
Z	impedance
Z_B	base value of the impedance
Z_{pu}	per-unit value of the impedance
ΔV	small voltage difference
δ	torque angle, load angle or transmission angle
μ	permeability
μ_0	permeability of free space
Φ	magnetic flux linkage
ϕ	phase angle
ω	angular frequency

Abbreviations

a.c.	alternating current
d.c.	direct current
e.m.f.	electromotive force
ln	natural logarithm
pu	per-unit
rev/min	revolutions per minute
r.m.s.	root mean square
VAr	volt-ampere reactive.

Bold italic type denotes the quantity is a phasor.

Chapter 1

Introduction

We may well begin by asking, 'what is an electric power system?'
An electric power system, or as it is sometimes called today, an
electric energy system, is the name given to a group of power
stations, transformers, switchgear and other components which
are interconnected by overhead lines and underground cables, to
supply consumers with electricity. Power systems developed many
years later than power generation. In the early years each power
station supplied its own local load. Some generators produced
alternating current (a.c.) and others direct current (d.c.). There was
soon rivalry between the advocates of a.c. and the advocates of d.c.,
but a.c. quickly prevailed. There was then a steady development of
generating stations until each large town or load centre had its own
station.

The advantages of alternating current are easy to appreciate. The
outstanding advantage is that the voltage can be stepped up or down
by using a transformer. This means that each part of a power system
can operate at its optimum voltage. Thus the generators can produce power at around 11 000 V to 22 000 V (11 kV to 22 kV) to suit
the designer. The loads can take power at 240 V, 415 V, etc. as
required by the consumer, and the transmission of power can take
place at 132 kV, 275 kV, 400 kV or even higher voltages. These
very high voltages are essential for the efficient transmission of
electric power. This is because, for a given power, as the voltage is
transformed up, the current is transformed down by the same factor.
Thus a 400 kV line carries only one-third as much current as a
132 kV line, if they are transmitting the same power. Power losses
in the lines are mainly due to resistive heating of the conductors
which is proportional to I^2R (current squared times resistance) so
that, for the same size of conductor, the losses in the 400 kV line
would be only about one-ninth of those in the 132 kV line. Another
advantage of alternating current compared with direct current is that
it is much easier to design and construct circuit breakers to interrupt
alternating current. The reason for this is explained in Chapter 4. In
Britain and the continent of Europe the system frequency is 50 Hz,
but in the American continent it is 60 Hz.

1

1.0 *Introduction*

Electricity is not itself a source of primary energy, but it is by far the most versatile and convenient form into which the primary energy of coal and oil, nuclear energy and the potential energy of stored water, can be transformed. Electricity can be converted into heat with 100 per cent efficiency and into mechanical motion with very high efficiency. This is done without producing any pollution or waste product of any kind. Electricity is also the only possible source of power for a wide range of electronic goods.

For any equipment, electricity generated in power stations is a much cheaper source of energy than primary batteries (dry cells). Secondary batteries offer a convenient way of making this energy available to portable equipment. If even better secondary batteries could be developed they would provide a very attractive way of powering small motor vehicles, particularly private cars. What is needed is a battery which is lighter, cheaper and longer lasting than present commercial batteries. The cost of running a car on electricity as compared with the cost of running it on petrol (gasoline), depends on the various efficiencies involved as well as the current prices of the fuels, but the cost of electricity to run a car is likely to be much less than the cost of petrol. There would be an additional advantage, if cars were charged overnight, in that the charging load would help to improve the power system load factor. The meaning of the system load factor is explained in Chapter 7.

In the USA a fairly large number of independent companies are responsible for generation, transmission and distribution of electricity, a notable exception being the Tennessee Valley Authority which is owned by the Federal Government. Although independent as electricity undertakings, their power systems are interconnected and the Government maintains a certain amount of control over their activities. By contrast, in Britain, the whole generation, transmission and distribution system is State-owned. The system in England and Wales is closely interconnected and has been for many years the largest closely interconnected system in the world. Consequently, certain aspects of power system control were unique to this system.

In England and Wales the generation and transmission of electricity is the responsibility of the Central Electricity Generating Board (C.E.G.B.). The C.E.G.B. supplies 12 Area Boards which distribute the electricity to consumers throughout England and Wales. In the southern part of Scotland, generation, transmission and distribution to consumers are all carried out by one authority, the South of Scotland Electricity Board (S.S.E.B.). Similarly, in the northern part of Scotland all three functions are the responsibility of one authority, the North of Scotland Hydro-Electric Board (N.S.H.E.B.). All these organisations work closely together and the whole transmission system in England, Wales and Scotland is interconnected and synchronised.

A rapid growth in the amount of electricity generated in industrial countries took place after the Second World War. In the USA, for example, during the period 1945 to 1970 generating capacity doubled approximately every 10 years. This represents an average increase each year of about 7 per cent on the previous year's total. However, during the 1970s the steady growth of the electricity industry has faltered due mainly to large increases in the price of oil especially, and coal to a lesser extent. This has affected the demand for electricity in three ways. Firstly, it has caused a recession in industrial activity which is reflected in a reduced demand for electrical power. Secondly, it has made many people energy conscious and they have made efforts to save all forms of energy, electricity included. Thirdly, it has made electricity less competitive than rival fuels, particularly natural gas, because the cost of electricity nearly always reflects the cost of the primary fuels from which it is derived. An exception to this rule, of course, is where most of the electricity is generated as hydro-electric power. There are few countries which are in this fortunate position.

Because of their very large size, power systems have a considerable impact on the environment. This takes a number of forms. Firstly, most modern power stations are very large and unless they are constructed underground they will be visible over a wide area, particularly if they have a chimney and cooling towers. A high chimney is necessary to dissipate the flue gases well away from the neighbourhood of the station and ensure that they are sufficiently diluted by atmospheric air before they reach ground level. Some critics claim that this merely transfers the pollution to another area or even to another country. There have been claims that acidic rain in Scandinavia, originating from the sulphur dioxide from tall chimneys in Britain, has inhibited the growth of trees in Norway and Sweden. The sulphur dioxide is produced when coal or oil containing sulphur is burnt in a power station. It is possible to remove the sulphur dioxide from the flue gases or prevent it from being formed, but not without creating other problems. Sometimes the large plumes which hang over power station cooling towers are mistaken for pollution. They are in fact nothing more than water vapour and can be looked upon as artificial clouds. Some environmentalists worry about the hot water discharged into rivers by thermal power stations. This can indeed upset the balance of life in the river, but in many cases it can provide conditions in which fish thrive. There could well be a case for using this warm water for fish farming on a large scale. Another possible use is in horticulture where the warm water could be used to heat greenhouses.

Another aspect of modern power systems which has a considerable impact on the environment, is the presence of an overhead power transmission system. With the increases in power-line voltages over the last 20 or 30 years, there has of necessity been an increase in the size of the towers or pylons which support the lines. Increases have also been made in the size and number of the conductors. Both of these factors make modern overhead lines more obtrusive. It is technically possible to put all the transmission system below ground using high-voltage cables. The reasons why this is not done are explained in Chapter 4. The C.E.G.B. has a statutory duty, when considering new developments, to take into account any effect which these developments may have on the natural beauty of the countryside or on features of special interest.

It seems likely that power systems will continue to grow both in overall size and in the size of individual components. It is unlikely, though, that the growth will be as rapid as it was during the 20 years from 1950 to 1970. Much depends on whether nuclear reactors, particularly the breeder, are allowed to provide a major contribution to the growth. The nuclear reactions which are useful for electric power generation, are described in Chapter 7.

Chapter 2
Three-phase systems

2.1 Advantages of three-phase

While domestic consumers nearly all take their electricity in the form of single-phase power, all large power systems use three phases. There are a number of advantages in having a three-phase system, namely: (i) Power and torque are constant in a three-phase motor or generator, which means that the machines will run more smoothly than single-phase machines in which the torque pulsates at twice the system frequency. (ii) For a given size, that is for a given amount of steel and copper, a three-phase machine has a greater output power. (iii) A three-phase transmission system will carry a greater power than a single-phase system, other things being equal. The reason for this will be explained later. The second and third points are really economic considerations, and because power systems are so large and costly, economic considerations influence this and many other aspects of power systems.

2.2 Star and delta connections

To help to understand a three-phase generator, consider first a primitive single-phase generator consisting of a coil of N turns and area A square metres, rotating in a magnetic field of flux density B tesla, as shown in Fig. 2.1. With the coil in the position shown in Fig. 2.1, the magnetic flux, Φ, linked by the coil is NAB cos θ weber. When the coil is rotating, $\theta = \omega t$, where ω is the angular frequency of rotation of the coil in radians per second, and t is the time in seconds. Therefore the magnetic flux linkage is given by:

$$\Phi = NAB \cos \omega t$$

By Faraday's law the induced electromotive force (e.m.f.), e, is equal

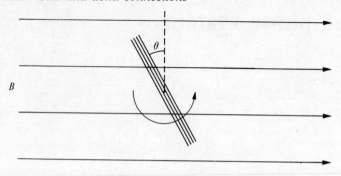

Fig. 2.1 Primitive single-phase generator.

to minus the rate of change of flux linkage, i.e.:

$$e = -\frac{d\Phi}{dt}$$

Therefore the e.m.f. is given by:

$$e = NAB\omega \sin \omega t \text{ volts}$$

The point to note is that the e.m.f. is sinusoidal and so can be represented as shown in Fig. 2.2. Suppose instead of just one coil we have three identical coils fixed together so that each makes an angle of 120° with the other two, as shown in Fig. 2.3. We now have a primitive three-phase generator, or rather, three coupled single-phase generators. Taken individually the e.m.f. in each coil will be as shown in Fig. 2.2, that is, just the same as before, but note that coil 2 must rotate through 120° to come to the position at present occupied by coil 1, and likewise coil 3 must rotate through 240°. This is another way of saying that the e.m.f. in coil 2 is later in phase, or is lagging, by 120° with respect to coil 1, and likewise the e.m.f. in coil 3 is lagging by 240° with respect to coil 1. This is illustrated by Fig. 2.4 which shows the time dependence of all three

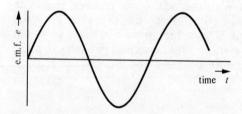

Fig. 2.2 E.M.F. from a primitive single-phase generator.

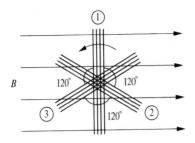

Fig. 2.3 Primitive three-phase generator.

e.m.fs. The three e.m.fs can be expressed also as:

$$e_1 = e_0 \sin \omega t$$
$$e_2 = e_0 \sin(\omega t - 120°)$$
$$e_3 = e_0 \sin(\omega t - 240°)$$
or $\quad e_3 = e_0 \sin(\omega t + 120°)$

where $e_0 = NAB\omega$. Note that although the angles in the brackets are expressed in degrees, they must be converted to radians (180° = π radians) if the expressions are used for numerical calculations. The last equation shows that we can regard the e.m.f. in coil 3 as leading coil 1 by 120° rather than lagging coil 1 by 240° which, of course, is exactly the same thing. To develop the three coupled single-phase generators of Fig. 2.3 into a three-phase generator, the ends of the coils must be connected together. There are two ways of doing this. The first, known as star connection, is arrived at by connecting together similar ends of the three coils to form what is called the star point. The three remaining ends are then brought out to form the three terminals of the three-phase generator. A conductor from the star point can also be brought out but this is not essential. By 'similar ends' is meant, for example, the ends of the coils at which the winding finished. This arrangement is shown in Fig. 2.5 where the dots show the ends of the coils at which the winding finished. The second arrangement, known as delta connection, is shown in Fig. 2.6. Here the coils from a loop, or delta, and provide just three

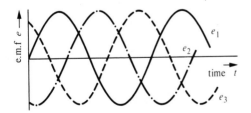

Fig. 2.4 E.M.Fs from a primitive three-phase generator.

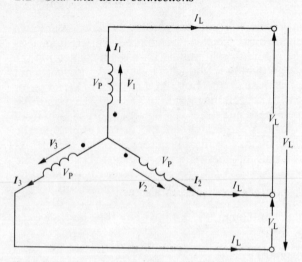

Fig. 2.5 Star connection of a three-phase generator.

terminals. There is no star point with a delta connection. The end of one coil is connected to the start of the next coil to form the loop. In Figs 2.5 and 2.6, V_p represents the magnitude of the voltage induced in each coil, while V_1, V_2 and V_3 are the phasors representing the voltages induced in coils 1, 2 and 3 respectively. Note that in each case the voltage phasors V_1, V_2 and V_3 are induced in the same direction with respect to the dots.

At this stage we must distinguish between phase and line quantities. The voltage across the ends of each coil is known as the phase voltage and its root mean square (r.m.s.) value denoted by V_p. Clearly $V_p = e_0/\sqrt{2}$ from the definition of r.m.s. From the symmetry

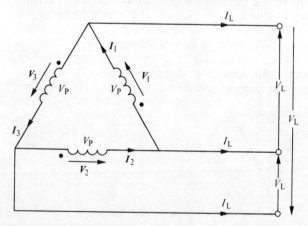

Fig. 2.6 Delta connection of a three-phase generator.

of the arrangement of the coils the r.m.s. voltages between any two of the three terminals have the same magnitude. This is known as the line voltage V_L. Figure 2.6 shows that for a delta connection the line voltage is equal to the phase voltage, However, V_p is clearly not equal to V_L for the star connection. In fact, $V_L = |V_1 - V_2|$ (or $|V_2 - V_3|$ or $|V_3 - V_1|$), i.e. the magnitude of $(V_1 - V_2)$, etc. and the relationship between these quantities can be seen more clearly from Fig. 2.7. In this diagram the lengths of the arrows represent the r.m.s. values of the voltages, while the orientations of the arrows show the phase relationships between the voltages. To obtain the relationship between V_L and V_P it is perhaps easier to consider Fig. 2.8 which is similar to Fig. 2.7 but with V_L transposed to the right-hand side.

From the triangle containing V_L, we have, by the sine rule:

$$\frac{V_L}{\sin 120°} = \frac{V_P}{\sin 30°}$$

$$\therefore \quad \frac{V_L}{\sqrt{3}/2} = \frac{V_P}{1/2}$$

$$\therefore \quad V_L = \sqrt{3}\,V_P$$

Note also that V_L leads V_1 by 30°.

The relation between V_L and V_P for a star connection can also be derived from the expressions for the instantaneous phase voltages,

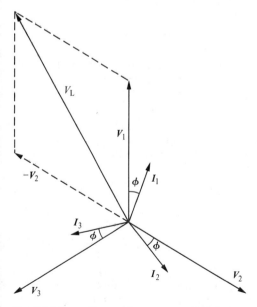

Fig. 2.7 Phasor diagram for a star-connected generator.

2.2 Star and delta connections

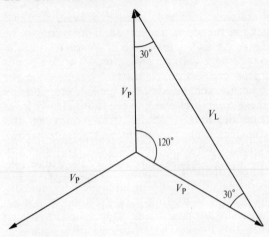

Fig. 2.8 Phasor diagram to show the relation between V_L and V_P for a star-connected generator.

as follows:

$$v_L = v_1 - v_2$$
$$\therefore \quad v_L = v_0 \sin \omega t - v_0 \sin(\omega t - 120°)$$
$$\therefore \quad v_L = 2v_0 \cos(\omega t - 60°)\sin 60°$$
$$\therefore \quad v_L = \sqrt{3}v_0 \cos(\omega t - 60°)$$
$$\text{or} \quad v_L = \sqrt{3}v_0 \sin(\omega t + 30°)$$

Hence the peak value of the line voltage is $\sqrt{3}$ times the peak value of the phase voltage. To obtain r.m.s. values we divide the peak value of each side by $\sqrt{2}$ and obtain:

$$V_L = \sqrt{3}V_P \quad \text{(star connection)}$$

The voltage quoted by engineers working with three-phase is always the line voltage, unless otherwise stated, and so the suffix L is often dropped.

Figure 2.5 shows that for a star connection the line current is equal to the phase current i.e. $I_L = I_P$. However, Fig. 2.6 clearly shows that I_L is not equal to I_P for a delta connection. The relationship between I_L and I_P for a delta connection can be found by methods very similar to those which were used to find the relationship between V_L and V_P for the star connection. In each phase, the phase current I_P will be lagging (or leading) the phase voltage V_P by an angle ϕ as shown in Fig. 2.7. Figure 2.6 shows that $I_L = |\boldsymbol{I}_1 - \boldsymbol{I}_3|$ (or $|\boldsymbol{I}_2 - \boldsymbol{I}_1|$ or $|\boldsymbol{I}_3 - \boldsymbol{I}_2|$) and consideration of a phasor diagram similar to Fig. 2.8, but drawn for line and phase currents,

10

yields:

$$\frac{I_\text{L}}{\sin 120°} = \frac{I_\text{P}}{\sin 30°}$$

$$\therefore \quad \frac{I_\text{L}}{\sqrt{3}/2} = \frac{I_\text{P}}{1/2}$$

$$\therefore \quad I_\text{L} = \sqrt{3} I_\text{P} \quad \text{(delta connection)}$$

The foregoing calculations assume the system is balanced, that is, there are no significant differences between the three phases. In other words the magnitudes of the three-phase voltages are essentially equal and each is displaced by 120°, or an angle very near to 120°, from the other two. This is true most of the time in power systems except near large single-phase loads. Unbalanced systems will not be considered in this book. The advantage of a balanced system is that we need only calculate what happens in one phase to know what happens in the whole system.

There is a special expression for the power in a three-phase system, which can easily be derived as follows. Thinking of one phase in isolation the power is, or course, the same as for a single-phase arrangement. Therefore, the power generated by one phase of a three-phase generator or absorbed by one phase of a three-phase load is $V_\text{P} I_\text{P} \cos \phi$, where ϕ is the phase angle between the voltage and current phasors. Each of the three phases generates (or absorbs) this power so the total power, P is given by:

$$P = 3 V_\text{P} I_\text{P} \cos \phi$$

For a star-connected generator or load we have shown that $V_\text{L} = \sqrt{3} V_\text{P}$ and $I_\text{L} = I_\text{P}$, so in terms of line quantities:

$$P = \sqrt{3} V_\text{L} I_\text{L} \cos \phi$$

For a delta-connected generator or load we have shown that $V_\text{L} = V_\text{P}$ and $I_\text{L} = \sqrt{3} I_\text{P}$, so in terms of line quantities again the power is given by:

$$P = \sqrt{3} V_\text{L} I_\text{L} \cos \phi$$

Since quantities quoted in three-phase circuits are assumed to be line quantities, unless otherwise stated, the expression for power in either a star or delta circuit can be written simply as:

$$P = \sqrt{3} VI \cos \phi$$

2.3   The grid

In the year 1926 the Central Electricity Board was set up in Britain to plan the interconnection of the larger and more efficient power stations which were in operation at that time. The work was done between 1928 and 1933 using a high-voltage network known as the grid, working at 132 kV, three-phase. The advantages of the grid were threefold. Firstly, fewer generators were required as reserve. To see that this is so, consider an isolated power station supplying its own local load. Suppose four generator sets are needed to meet the maximum load. A fifth set must be provided in case one of the four unexpectedly fails. Alternatively, if the power station were linked to a similar nearby one, only one spare set out of nine would be needed, instead of one spare set out of five. Secondly, fewer generators were needed to run without load (spinning reserve) to take care of sudden unexpected jumps in the demand. These could be shared, by the same reasoning as above. Thirdly, the most economical plant could be used at times of low demand. From 1926 to 1936 spare plant dropped from 70 to 26 per cent and the average cost of generation dropped from 50 pence per TJ to 22 pence per TJ. The grid was mainly responsible for these spectacular reductions. When the grid was completed it had about 5 000 route kilometres of overhead lines which were operated in seven independent regions. Each region had enough generating stations to supply its own area. The one disadvantage of the grid, or indeed of any form of interconnection of generating plant, is that more current flows into a fault (short-circuit), so circuit breakers able to interrupt larger currents are needed. Originally the 132 kV switchgear had a rating of 1.5 GVA, later 2.5 GVA and finally 3.5 GVA. The significance of these figures will be explained later.

2.4 The supergrid

In 1948 it was realised that the benefits achieved as a result of using the grid would be even greater if the whole of Britain were interconnected. Thus a 275 kV network was superimposed on the 132 kV grid. The 275 kV system is known in the industry as the supergrid. It was built to carry large quantities of power right across the country. This is referred to as the bulk transmission of power and allows power stations to be built at the most economic sites which may be a long way from the load centre which they supply. It also allows nuclear stations to be built well away from large centres of population.

Some of the main features of the supergrid in England and Wales are:

1. A complex network in the London area, a large industrialised urban area.
2. A complex network round Birmingham, also a large industrialised urban area.

3. A complex network in the area surrounded by the cities of Manchester, Leeds, York, Hull, Nottingham and Sheffield. This area includes the power stations built on the Yorkshire, Nottinghamshire and Derbyshire coalfield.
4. Links between the above three regions.
5. Links between South Wales and London.
6. Links between South-west England and London.
7. Links from the North Wales nuclear and pumped storage stations to the Merseyside and Manchester areas.
8. Links to Scotland.

The building of the supergrid enabled the proportion of spare plant to be reduced to 17 per cent.

Since 1965 expansion of the supergrid has been made at 400 kV and some of the earlier 275 kV lines have been uprated to 400 kV. The higher voltage is more economical for large power transfers, and the addition of 400 kV lines resulted in fewer lines being required than would have been the case if the voltage had been kept down to 275 kV.

Problems

1. A star-connected alternator has an open-circuit terminal voltage of 3.3 kV. What is the generated e.m.f. in each phase?   (1.9 kV)

2. A star-connected three-phase load absorbs 40 kW at a power factor of 0.875 lagging when supplied from a 6.6 kV line. Calculate: (i) the phase voltage; (ii) the line current.   (3.8 kV; 4.0 A)

3. A delta-connected three-phase load of $(80 + j60)\ \Omega$ per phase is connected to a 440 V three-phase supply. Calculate: (i) the phase current; (ii) the line current; (iii) the total power consumption.   (4.4 A; 7.62 A; 4.65 kW)

Chapter 3

Real power, apparent power and reactive power

In a power system there are lines, cables, loads, etc. and each of these has its own impedance Z which can be represented as a phasor by a complex number, i.e. $Z = R + jX$, where R is the resistive component of Z, and X is the reactive component. For inductive components jX will be positive, while for capacitive components jX will be negative. Also each generator in the system which is producing power will be delivering current at some power factor $\cos \phi$ which will differ for each machine. In principle, given the voltage, power and power factor for every component of the system, it would be possible to make calculations of the power flow or current flow in every part of the system. However, calculations made this way are very difficult, mainly because there is no simple correlation between the power factors of the different components. Instead, power engineers work with reactive power, rather than power factor. This makes the calculations easier because there is a simple correlation between the reactive power in different components, but first let us define the different types of power.

The proper power, which is just called power in other branches of electrical engineering, needs an adjective to distinguish it from the other sorts of power. It is sometimes called active power, sometimes real power, but in this book it will be referred to as real power. In a single-phase system with sinusoidal quantities it can be calculated from the product of the voltage, the current and the cosine of the phase angle between them, i.e. $VI \cos \phi$. It can also be thought of as the product of the voltage and the component of current in phase with the voltage. Real power is denoted by the symbol P and is measured in watts. Another useful quantity is the product of the voltage and current, taking no account of the phase angle. This is known as the apparent power. It is denoted by the symbol S and is measured in volt-amperes. Apparent power is useful for specifying the rating of components in which the maximum voltage is fixed and the maximum current is fixed, irrespective of the phase angle. Calculations of apparent power are also useful as an intermediate step in finding the real power and the reactive power. The reactive power is the product of the voltage, the current and the *sine* of the phase angle between them, i.e. $VI \sin \phi$. It may also be thought of as the product of the voltage and the component of current in quadrature with the voltage. Reactive power is denoted by the symbol Q and is measured in volt-amperes reactive (VAr), sometimes spoken of as 'vars'. There is a tendency for power engineers to refer to these three types of power by their units rather than their names, and they speak of, for example, 'the volt-amp rating', 'an increase in vars' and 'the megawatt output'.

In three-phase systems the component voltage is conventionally replaced by the line voltage which introduces a factor of $\sqrt{3}$ into the expressions for power. To summarise we have then:

Real power, $P = \sqrt{3}\,VI \cos \phi$ measured in watts.
Apparent power, $S = \sqrt{3}\,VI$ measured in volt-amperes.
Reactive power, $Q = \sqrt{3}\,VI \sin \phi$ measured in volt-amperes reactive.

Thus $P = S \cos \phi$ and $Q = S \sin \phi$. (A quantity met with in more advanced studies of power systems is complex power or vector power which is defined as $P + jQ$.)

The sign of Q is arbitrary, but by convention is taken as positive at a load when the power factor is lagging. The convenience of this convention is that a load with some inductance (most loads are inductive) will consume real power and consume reactive power. A capacitor is thought of as supplying reactive power to the system, rather than consuming negative reactive power. Remember, a capacitor takes a leading power factor.

In any one second, taking a power system as a whole, the total electrical energy generated must equal the total electrical energy consumed. This follows from the fact that electrical energy cannot be stored in the system. The energy lost or gained per second is the power so *the total of the real power generated equals the total of the real power consumed.* It can also be shown that *the total of the reactive power generated equals the total of the reactive power consumed.*

It will be shown later that this last relation makes the concept of reactive power very useful in power system calculations. We shall see shortly how to make use of these relationships, but first consider single components.

Example 3.1

How much reactive power is consumed by a perfect inductor?

Let the voltage across the inductor be V, the current through it be I and the reactance be X_L. By definition the reactive power Q is given by:

$$Q = VI \sin \phi$$

3.0 *Real power, apparent power and reactive power*

Now for a perfect inductor the current lags the voltage by 90° giving $\sin \phi = 1$.

By Ohm's law $V = IX_L$

giving $Q = I^2 X_L$

Example 3.2

How much reactive power is generated by a perfect capacitor?

Let the voltage across the capacitor be V, the current through it be I and the reactance X_C. As before:

$Q = VI \sin \phi$

Now for a perfect capacitor the current leads the voltage by 90° giving $\sin \phi = 1$.

By Ohm's law $V = IX_C$

giving $Q = I^2 X_C$

However, with a capacitor it is often more convenient to work in terms of the voltage rather than the current. Using Ohm's law again gives:

$$Q = \frac{V^2}{X_C}$$

Note that in this example the current is leading the voltage by 90° and in the previous example it was lagging by 90°. This 180° phase change is accounted for by regarding the reactive power in an inductor as being consumed and regarding the reactive power in a capacitor as being generated.

Consider now a simple problem solved first by using phase angles and then by using reactive power.

Example 3.3

A three-phase 50 Hz generator supplies power to a load through a transmission line of series impedance $(50 + j500)\ \Omega$ per phase. The load consumes 50 kW at 11 kV with a power factor of 0.8 lagging. Three capacitors, each 0.5 μF, are connected in star across the load to improve the power factor. Measurements of the line current show it to be 2.8 A. Find the generator phase angle.

Since the system is balanced, consider just one phase to neutral. The circuit of one phase is shown in Fig. 3.1. Let the load voltage be the reference phasor. Find the real and imaginary parts of the load current phasor, I_L. For a three-phase

16

3.0 Real power, apparent power and reactive power

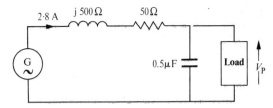

Fig. 3.1 Circuit diagram of one phase to neutral for example 3.3.

system the power is given by: $P = \sqrt{3}\,VI_L \cos \phi$

$$\therefore \; I_L = \frac{P}{\sqrt{3}\,V \cos \phi} = \frac{50 \times 10^3}{\sqrt{3} \times 11\,000 \times 0.8} = 3.28 \text{ A}$$

As a phasor $I_L = 3.28 \cos \phi - j3.28 \sin \phi$ (minus j because the current is lagging)

$$\therefore \; I_L = 3.28 \times 0.8 - j3.28 \times 0.6$$

$$\therefore \; I_L = 2.624 - j1.968 \text{ A}$$

The voltage across one phase of the load is given by:

$$V_P = \frac{V}{\sqrt{3}} = \frac{11\,000}{\sqrt{3}} = 6\,351 \text{ V}$$

We cannot find the voltage drop phasor along the transmission line by multiplying 2.8 by $(50 + j500)$ because we do not know the phase angle of the 2.8 A line current. Instead we must add the capacitor current to the load current.

The capacitor current is given by:

$$I_C = \frac{V_P}{X_C} = j\omega CV_P = j2\pi 50 \times 0.5 \times 10^{-6} \times 6\,351 = j0.998 \text{ A}$$

The total current $I_L + I_C$ is also the generator current I_G so

$$I_G = I_L + I_C = 2.624 - j1.968 + j0.998$$

$$\therefore I_G = 2.624 - j0.970 \text{ A}$$

Hence the generator current lags the load voltage by:

$$\arctan \left(\frac{0.970}{2.624} \right) = 20.3°$$

(Check that $|I_G| = 2.8$. $|I_G| = \sqrt{2.624^2 + 0.970^2} = 2.798$). We still need to find the generator voltage angle. To do this we add, as phasors, the load voltage and the voltage drop along the line. The voltage drop along the line V_Z is given by:

$$V_Z = I_G Z = (2.624 - j0.970) \times (50 + j500) = 616 + j1\,264$$

17

The generator voltage is

$$V_G = V_Z + V_P = 616 + j1\,264 + 6\,351 + j0 = 6\,967 + j1\,264 \text{ V}$$

so V_G leads V_L by:

$$\arctan \left(\frac{1264}{6967}\right) = 1.28°$$

Now we have established that I_G lags V_L by 20.3° and V_G leads V_L by 10.28° so the generator phase angle is 20.3° + 10.28° = 30.6° lagging.

Now see how much easier the calculation is using real and reactive power. These may be written like a profit and loss balance. The real power consumed:

$$\text{in the load} = 50\,000 \text{ W}$$
$$\text{in the line} = 3 \times I^2 R = 3 \times 2.8^2 \times 50 = \quad 1\,176 \text{ W}$$

(Note the 3 here because there are three lines in a three-phase system.)

The total real power consumed in the whole system = $\overline{51\,176}$ W.

This, of course, must be equal to the total real power generated, P_G.

Now find the reactive power consumed.

Since $P = \sqrt{3}\,VI \cos\phi$ and $Q = \sqrt{3}\,VI \sin\phi$ then $Q = P \tan\phi$. In this case $\tan\phi = 0.75$.

The reactive power consumed:

$$\text{in the load} = 50\,000 \times 0.75 = 37\,500 \text{ VAr}$$
$$\text{in the line} = 3 \times I^2 X = 3 \times 2.8^2 \times 500 = 11\,760 \text{ VAr}$$
$$\text{Subtotal} \quad 49\,260 \text{ VAr}$$

less the reactive power generated in the capacitors
$= 3V_P^2/X_C = V^2/X_C$ (because $V = \sqrt{3}\,V_P$)

$$V^2/X_C = 11\,000^2 \times 2\pi50 \times 0.5 \times 10^{-6} = \underline{19\,007} \text{ VAr}$$
$$\text{Total} \quad \underline{30\,253} \text{ VAr}$$

This, of course, must be equal to the reactive power generated, Q_G.

Now from the definitions of P and Q it is easily shown that $\phi = \arctan Q/P$, so the generator phase angle $\phi = \arctan$ 30 253/51 176 = 30.6° lagging.

This is a much easier calculation than the previous one.

Problems

1. An impedance of $(40 + j30)$ Ω carries a current of 10 A. Calculate: (i) the real power consumed; (ii) the reactive power consumed.
                                              (4 kW; 3 kVAr)

2. A capacitor of 2 μF is connected to a 240 V, single-phase, 50 Hz supply. Calculate the reactive power generated by the capacitor.

(36.2 VAr)

3. A star-connected load consisting of a resistor of 80 Ω and an inductor of 0.191 H in each phase, is connected to a 415 V, three-phase, 50 Hz supply. Calculate: (i) the line current I; (ii) the real power P consumed by the load; and (iii) the reactive power Q consumed by the load. From P and Q calculate the load phase angle ϕ, and show that $P = \sqrt{3} VI \cos \phi$ and $Q = \sqrt{3} VI \sin \phi$.

(2.4 A; 1 378 W; 1 033 VAr; 36.9°)

4. Three capacitors, each 5 μF, are connected in delta across a 3.3 kV, three-phase line. If the system frequency is 50 Hz, calculate how much reactive power is generated by the capacitors. If the system voltage falls by 5 per cent what will be the corresponding fall in reactive power generation? (51.3 kVAr; 9.75 per cent)

5. Each phase of a length of 132 kV overhead power line can be represented by a series inductive reactance of 0.41 Ω and a shunt capacitive reactance to ground of 340 kΩ. At what current does the line neither generate nor consume reactive power? This condition is known as the natural loading of the line. (204 A)

6. A star-connected load of $(75 + j48)$ Ω per phase is supplied from a 50 Hz alternator through a transmission line of $(5 + j12)$ Ω per conductor. Three capacitors, each 5 μF, are connected in delta across the alternator terminals. If the alternator terminal voltage is 440 V, calculate: (i) the real power; (ii) the reactive power, generated by the alternator and hence find the alternator power factor.

(1 549 W; 249 VAr; 0.987 lagging)

Chapter 4
Components of a power system

4.1 The alternator

In essence, an alternator consists of a coil which is rotated in a steady magnetic field. As explained in section 2.2 an e.m.f. is induced in the coil and the variation of the e.m.f., e, with time, t, is given by $e = NAB\omega \sin \omega t$, where A is the area of the coil, N is the number of turns on the coil, B is the flux density of the magnetic field and ω is the angular frequency of rotation of the coil. For a three-phase alternator, three symmetrically arranged coils are required. The steady magnetic field can be produced by passing a direct current through the field windings. However, large alternators are constructed the other way round, in that they have a rotating magnetic field and the generated e.m.fs are induced in the fixed stator coils. The strength of the rotating field is controlled by a direct current fed to the rotor (the rotating part) via slip rings. These perform a function similar to that of the commutator in a d.c. machine, but because they are not segmented the current through the rotor winding does not reverse as it rotates. The current in the rotor is referred to as the excitation of the machine. It is much easier to feed the direct current to the rotor because, with this arrangement, the slip rings carry a much smaller current at a lower voltage than they would if the exciting field were stationary. For example the current and voltage in a typical 500 MW alternator are:

Stator, 15 000 A at 12 700 V per phase.
Rotor, 4 000 A at 500 V.

Before an alternator can be connected to the grid system, four conditions must be satisfied simultaneously.
The alternator must:

1. Have the same phase sequence as the grid voltages.
2. Have the same frequency as the grid voltages.
3. Have the same voltage at the circuit-breaker terminals as the grid.
4. Be in phase with the grid.

20

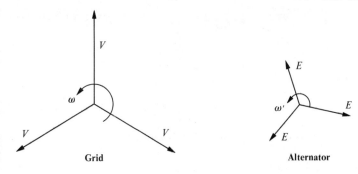

Fig. 4.1 Grid and alternator voltage phasors before synchronising.

At first only condition (1) will be satisfied: this is taken care of at the installation stage. Before the remaining conditions are satisfied, the three grid voltages and the three alternator voltages will be typically as shown in Fig. 4.1 where V is the r.m.s. phase voltage of the grid at the circuit-breaker terminals, and E is the r.m.s. phase voltage of the generated e.m.f. The frequency can be increased by feeding more steam to the turbine and thus increasing the rotational speed of the turbine and alternator. The generated voltages can be increased by increasing the excitation of the alternator. The phase of the generated voltages can be matched to the phase of the grid voltages by allowing a very small frequency difference to persist. The two voltages will then very slowly drift in and out of phase in a cyclical sequence. It is then just a matter of waiting for the exact instant when they are precisely in phase, and promptly closing the circuit breaker. When the frequency, voltage and phase of the alternator have been correctly adjusted, conditions will be as shown in Fig. 4.2. After the circuit breaker has been closed, the alternator is said to be synchronised to the grid. In this condition its output voltage and frequency are locked to the system values and cannot be

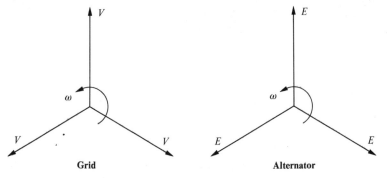

Fig. 4.2 Grid and alternator voltage phasors ready for synchronising.

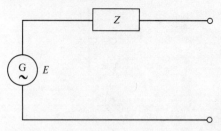

Fig. 4.3 Equivalent circuit of one phase of a synchronised alternator.

changed by any action on the alternator, so long as it remains in synchronism with the grid. This is known as working on infinite busbars.

Each phase of a synchronised alternator can be represented by the equivalent circuit shown in Fig. 4.3. In many applications this can be simplified by omitting the resistive component of Z so that the equivalent circuit becomes that shown in Fig. 4.4. The parameter X is known as the synchronous reactance, sometimes denoted by X_s, and is constant in the normal operating situation.

Immediately after synchronising, the situation is as shown in Fig. 4.5 where the alternator is neither feeding power to, nor absorbing power from, the grid. The steam power going into the turbine which is driving the alternator is just sufficient to overcome the losses of the turbine and generator. The word 'generator' is used here to include the alternator and its exciter which provides the alternator field. If more steam is fed into the turbine one might expect the set to speed up but this is not possible when it is synchronised to the grid. Alternatively, one might expect the generator terminal voltage to rise but again this cannot happen if the generator is synchronised to the grid. What *does* happen is shown in Fig. 4.6. The generator e.m.f., E, now leads the grid voltage by an angle δ, known as the torque angle or load angle. As a consequence current, and hence power, is fed into the grid. Figure 4.7 shows a simple equivalent circuit for one phase where the load is the grid, as seen from the generator terminals. Figure 4.8 is the phasor diagram for this circuit and it shows that I is almost in phase with V, for a small angle δ,

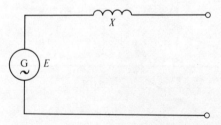

Fig. 4.4 Simplified equivalent circuit of one phase of a synchronised alternator.

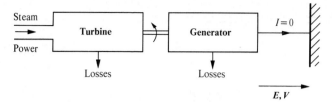

Fig. 4.5 Turbine generator synchronised but supplying no power.

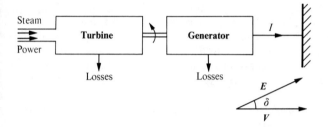

Fig. 4.6 Turbine generator supplying real power to the grid.

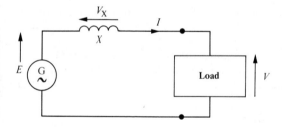

Fig. 4.7 Equivalent circuit of one phase of the generator and grid load.

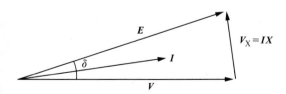

Fig. 4.8 Phasor diagram showing how real power is fed to the grid.

4.1 The alternator

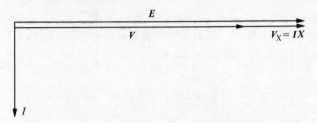

Fig. 4.9 Phasor diagram showing how reactive power is generated.

and hence real power is fed into the grid. Note that I is perpendicular to V_x because X is assumed to be a perfect inductor.

Reverting to the situation shown in Fig. 4.5, what happens if the steam flow is unchanged but the alternator excitation is increased? This must increase the generated e.m.f. because an increase in excitation causes an increase in the magnetic field flux density, B in the equation $e = NAB\omega \sin \omega t$. The phasor diagram, Fig. 4.9, shows that again current is fed into the grid, but this time the current is lagging the grid voltage by 90°, hence no real power is produced but reactive power is supplied to the grid.

Current also flows if the excitation is *reduced* but now, as shown in Fig. 4.10, the current flows in the opposite direction and so reactive power from the grid is absorbed by the generator. As before there is no flow of real power.

A more normal mode of operation of a turbine generator is somewhere between the extremes of Figs. 4.8 and 4.9, that is to say, the generator produces both real power and reactive power. This is shown in Fig. 4.11.

It is clear from the foregoing that the amount of real power produced depends on the torque angle. An expression for the real power P and the reactive power Q can be deduced as follows from the phasor diagram Fig. 4.11.

$$\boldsymbol{E} = \boldsymbol{V} + \boldsymbol{IX} \quad \text{(phasors)}$$

or $\quad \boldsymbol{I} = \dfrac{\boldsymbol{E}}{\boldsymbol{X}} - \dfrac{\boldsymbol{V}}{\boldsymbol{X}} \quad \text{(phasors)}$

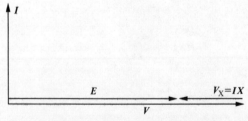

Fig. 4.10 Phasor diagram showing how reactive power is absorbed.

24

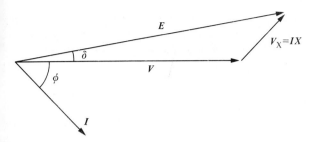

Fig. 4.11 Phasor diagram showing how real and reactive power are generated.

Expressing the phasors in polar form gives:

$$I = \frac{E\angle\delta}{X\angle 90°} - \frac{V\angle 0°}{X\angle 90°}$$

or $\quad I = \frac{E}{X}\angle(\delta - 90°) - \frac{V}{X}\angle -90°$

Turning from polar to Cartesian notation we have:

$$I = \frac{E}{X}\cos(\delta - 90°) + j\frac{E}{X}\sin(\delta - 90°) - \frac{V}{X}\cos(-90°) - j\frac{V}{X}\sin(-90°)$$

Now the output real power $= V \times$ (real part of I) or

$$P = \frac{VE}{X}\cos(\delta - 90°)$$

or $\quad P = \dfrac{VE}{X}\sin\delta$ watts per phase $\qquad \ldots$ (i)

Also the output reactive power $= V \times$ (minus imaginary part of I) or

$$Q = V\left\{-\frac{E}{X}\sin(\delta - 90°) + \frac{V}{X}\sin(-90°)\right\}$$

or $\quad Q = \dfrac{VE}{X}\cos\delta - \dfrac{V^2}{X}$ volt-amperes reactive per phase $\qquad \ldots$ (ii)

The expression (i) and (ii) derived above were obtained by considering one phase only so they should strictly speaking be written:

$$P = \frac{V_P E_P}{X}\sin\delta \text{ watts per phase}$$

and $\quad Q = \dfrac{V_P E_P}{X}\cos\delta - \dfrac{V_P^2}{X}$ volt-amperes reactive per phase

To obtain the total power we multiply each expression by 3. We can also substitute the more usual line quantities, using $V_P = V/\sqrt{3}$ and $E_P = E/\sqrt{3}$. The two $\sqrt{3}$ terms in the denominator of each expression cancel the 3 in the numerator and the expressions remain unchanged. Thus:

$$P = \frac{VE}{X} \sin \delta \text{ watts}$$

and $$Q = \frac{VE}{X} \cos \delta - \frac{V^2}{X} \text{ volt-amperes reactive}$$

where E and V are line values.

4.2   Overhead lines

Most of the electric power which is generated in Britain is transmitted on the 275 kV and 400 kV supergrid. The supergrid conductors are suspended from insulator strings which in turn are carried on towers about 50 m high spaced about 400 m apart. Each tower or pylon usually carries two three-phase lines. Two types of tower may be distinguished: firstly, the straight-run tower which supports only the weight of the conductors and insulators; and secondly, the deviation tower which also resists some of the conductor tension.

The insulator strings on the grid and the supergrid, consist of from 6 to 22 elements in series. Each element is in essence a glass or porcelain disc with a metal cap on top and a metal pin on the underside. The pin fits into the cap of the next element below.

The conductors are usually stranded steel-cored aluminium. That is, they consist of a few steel strands in the centre, surrounded by a larger number of aluminium strands. The steel provides the tensile strength while the aluminium provides good electrical conductivity.

Aluminium is chosen because it has a higher conductivity, for a given weight, than copper and is also relatively cheap. A typical 650 A conductor has 7 central steel strands and 54 aluminium strands, both of which are about 3 mm in diameter. The strands are coated in grease during manufacture of the conductor to minimise oxidation of the metals.

The 132 kV grid conductors are used singly, but the 275 kV supergrid conductors are mounted on their insulators in pairs with a spacing of about 30 cm. This is known as bundling of the conductors. The 400 kV system has either two or four conductors per bundle. There are three advantages of bundling as compared with the same volume of metal in the form of a single conductor. Firstly, the bundle has a lower inductance. Secondly, there is a lower voltage gradient at the surface: this is an advantage because a high-voltage gradient (electric field) at the surface of a conductor promotes corona discharges which waste power and produce radio interference. Thirdly, bundled conductors can carry a larger current due to the improved cooling resulting from the larger surface area.

Table 4.1 shows the apparent power and current carrying capacity of various overhead lines in Britain. The figures given are for a conductor temperature restricted to 50°C and for average conditions. In winter the ratings are about 22 per cent higher and in summer about 22 per cent lower. This is because the ambient temperature affects the cooling of the conductors

Table 4.1 Carrying capacity per circuit of overhead lines

Voltage (kV)	Number of conductors per bundle	Nominal area of aluminium per conductor, actual area in brackets (mm²)	Capacity (MVA)	Current (A)
132	1	175 (183)	100	450
132	1	400 (429)	150	650
275	2	175 (183)	430	900
275	2	400 (429)	620	1 300
400	2	400 (429)	900	1 300
400	4	400 (429)	1 800	2 600

In certain circumstances the conductor temperatures can be allowed to reach 65°C or even 75°C with a consequent increase in the carrying capacity of the lines.

The equivalent circuit for one phase of a short overhead line is shown in Fig. 4.12, where L is the series inductance, R the series resistance, C the shunt capacitance and R_0 the leakage resistance. Values for the resistance R and the reactances of L and C at 50 Hz are given in Table 4.2 for 132 kV and 400 kV lines.

Although it is convenient to think of a line in terms of a lumped inductance, a lumped capacitance and a lumped resistance as shown in Fig. 4.12, in reality these parameters are distributed evenly over the whole length of the line. For a short line the single lumped representation is quite satisfactory but for longer lines, say over 100 km, as used in the USA, the USSR and many other countries, a more exact representation is required.

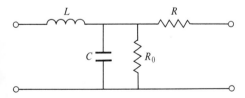

Fig. 4.12 Equivalent circuit for one phase of a short overhead line.

Table 4.2 Resistance and reactance per kilometre
length of one phase of overhead lines in Britain

Line	132 kV	275 kV	400 kV
	1×175 mm^2	2×400 mm^2	4×400 mm^2
R	0.178 Ω	0.039 Ω	0.020 Ω
X_L	j0.40 Ω	j0.32 Ω	j0.278 Ω
X_C	−j350 kΩ	−j275 kΩ	−j245 kΩ

The figures 1×175 mm^2, 2×400 mm^2 and 4×400 mm^2 refer to
the number of conductors per bundle and the nominal cross-
sectional area of the aluminium conductors. The value of R_0, the
leakage resistance, is not given in the table because it is very
variable. It depends on atmospheric conditions and the cleanliness
of the insulators, but a typical value is 200 MΩ, so R_0 may be
neglected in the equivalent circuit.

Taking the values of X_L and X_C for a 1 km length of the 132 kV
line from Table 4.2, the reactive power absorbed in the series
reactance at a full-load current of 450 A is 81 kVAr, and the
reactive power generated in the shunt capacitance is only 17 kVAr,
so, to a rough approximation, the capacitance can be neglected
giving the equivalent circuit shown in Fig. 4.13. Also, since the
series resistance is small compared with the reactance, neglecting
the resistance leads to an error of less than 10 per cent in the series
impedance. The line may therefore be represented very simply by
the circuit of Fig. 4.14, where V_S is the sending-end voltage and V_R
is the receiving-end voltage. Note, however, that neither Fig. 4.13
nor Fig. 4.14 is valid at currents much below full-load. Both are, of
course, completely wrong on no-load. On no-load the shunt capacitance dominates. Note also that Fig. 4.14 is the same equivalent
circuit as that for an alternator if V_S replaces the alternator e.m.f.
The expression for the real power carried by the line is therefore the
same as that for the real power generated by an alternator with V_S
in place of E. The expression is:

$$P = \frac{V_S V_R \sin \delta}{X}$$

In the case of a line, δ is known as the transmission angle.

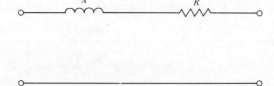

Fig. 4.13 Simplified equivalent circuit for one phase of a short overhead line.

28

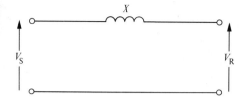

Fig. 4.14 Approximate equivalent circuit for one phase of a short overhead line.

As explained in section 4.1, the expression for P is valid in both single-phase and three-phase circuits. In a single-phase circuit V_S and V_R are the sending-end and receiving-end phase voltages, but in a three-phase circuit V_S and V_R are the sending-end and receiving-end line voltages. In each case P is the total real power carried by the line.

Line reactance X: single-phase

An expression for the inductance of a single-phase overhead line is a standard derivation to be found in books on electromagnetism. Suppose each of the two conductors has a radius r and their centres are separated by a distance d. It can be shown that:

$$L = \frac{\mu}{\pi}\left\{\frac{1}{4} + \ln\frac{(d-r)}{r}\right\} \text{ henrys per metre length}$$

In air $\mu = \mu_0 = 4\pi \times 10^{-7}$ H/m and so:

$$L = 4 \times 10^{-7} \times \left\{\tfrac{1}{4} + \ln(d/r)\right\} \text{ henrys per metre if } d \gg r.$$

The term $\tfrac{1}{4}$ comes from the internal flux linkage within the conductors. For a 50 Hz system the line reactance, X_L, is therefore given by:

$$X_L = 4\pi \times 10^{-5}\left\{\tfrac{1}{4} + \ln(d/r)\right\} \text{ ohms per metre}$$

The calculation of the line reactance for a three-phase line is difficult except in the special case of equilateral spacing.

Line reactance X: balanced three-phase with equilateral spacing.

Let the cross-section of the line be represented by Fig. 4.15 where the conductors have radius r and spacing d.

Consider a 1 m length of the line.

Let the height from the ground be h where $h \gg d$.
Let conductor 1 carry a current I_1.
Let conductor 2 carry a current I_2.
Let conductor 3 carry a current I_3.

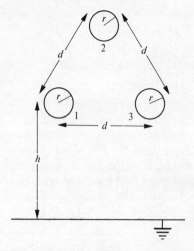

Fig. 4.15 Cross-section of a three-phase line with equilateral spacing.

Consider the inductance of phase 1 with respect to neutral. In a balanced system this is the inductance with respect to ground. First find the flux linkages. The internal flux linkage in conductor 1 is:

$$\frac{\mu \mathbf{I}_1}{8\pi}$$

The external flux linkage from conductor 1 is:

$$\int_{r}^{h} \frac{\mu \mathbf{I}_1}{2\pi x}\, dx = \frac{\mu \mathbf{I}_1}{2\pi} \ln\left(\frac{h}{r}\right)$$

The flux between conductor 1 and ground due to the current $\mathbf{I}_2$ is:

$$\int_{d}^{(h+0.87d)} \frac{\mu \mathbf{I}_2}{2\pi x}\, dx = \frac{\mu \mathbf{I}_2}{2\pi} \ln\left(\frac{h+0.87d}{d}\right) = \frac{\mu \mathbf{I}_2}{2\pi} \ln\left(\frac{h}{d}\right) \quad \text{(approximately)}$$

The flux between conductor 1 and ground due to the current $\mathbf{I}_3$ is:

$$\int_{d}^{h} \frac{\mu \mathbf{I}_3}{2\pi x}\, dx = \frac{\mu \mathbf{I}_3}{2\pi} \ln\left(\frac{h}{d}\right)$$

The total flux linkage, Φ, for conductor 1 is given by:

$$\Phi = \frac{\mu}{2\pi} \left\{ \frac{\mathbf{I}_1}{4} + \mathbf{I}_1 \ln\left(\frac{h}{r}\right) + \mathbf{I}_2 \ln\left(\frac{h}{d}\right) + \mathbf{I}_3 \ln\left(\frac{h}{d}\right) \right\} \text{ webers per metre}$$

But $I_1 + I_2 + I_3 = 0$ in a balanced system,

$\therefore \quad I_2 + I_3 = -I_1$

$\therefore \qquad \Phi = \dfrac{\mu}{2\pi} \left[\dfrac{I_1}{4} + I_1 \left\{ \ln\left(\dfrac{h}{r}\right) - \ln\left(\dfrac{h}{d}\right) \right\} \right]$ webers per metre

$\therefore \qquad \Phi = \dfrac{\mu}{2\pi} I_1 \{\tfrac{1}{4} + \ln(d/r)\}$ webers per metre per phase

By definition the inductance, L, is given by:

$\quad L = \Phi / I_1$

$\therefore \quad L = \dfrac{\mu}{2\pi} \{\tfrac{1}{4} + \ln(d/r)\}$ henrys per metre

In air $\mu = \mu_0 = 4\pi \times 10^{-7}$ H/m,

$\therefore \quad L = 2 \times 10^{-7} \{\tfrac{1}{4} + \ln(d/r)\}$ henrys per metre per phase

For a 50 Hz system the line reactance, X_L, is therefore given by:

$X_L = 2\pi \times 10^{-5} \{\tfrac{1}{4} + \ln(d/r)\}$ ohms per metre per phase

Note this is half of the value for a single-phase line and does not depend on the value of h, provided h is large.

When the conductors of a three-phase line are not spaced equilaterally the problem of finding the inductance becomes much more difficult. The flux linkages and hence the inductances of each phase are not equal. A different inductance in each phase results in an unbalanced circuit. On a long line this can be overcome by interchanging the positions of the conductors at convenient points, e.g. substations. The average inductance per phase can then be calculated by substituting d_{eq} for d in the expression above where:

$d_{eq} = (d_{12} \times d_{23} \times d_{31})^{1/3}$

Here d_{12} is the distance between conductors 1 and 2,
$\qquad d_{23}$ is the distance between conductors 2 and 3
and d_{31} is the distance between conductors 3 and 1.

A three-phase transmission system will carry a greater power than a single-phase system, other things being equal. To show that this is so, consider a double-circuit overhead power line, i.e. a system with six independent conductors. This is the usual type of overhead line in Britain.

Suppose each conductor can carry current up to I_{max} amperes r.m.s., and the system can safely withstand a line-to-line voltage up to V_{max} volts r.m.s. The six conductors can be used as two three-phase circuits. The maximum power that can be carried by one three-phase circuit, P, is given by:

$P = \sqrt{3} V_{max} I_{max}$ watts

Two three-phase circuits can carry a maximum power P_3, given by:

$$P_3 = 2\sqrt{3}\,V_{max}I_{max} \text{ watts}$$

Alternatively the six conductors can be used to make three single-phase circuits. The maximum power in each single phase circuit P' is given by:

$$P' = V_{max}I_{max} \text{ watts}$$

so three circuits can carry a maximum power P_1 given by:

$$P_1 = 3V_{max}I_{max} \text{ watts}$$

Note, P_3 is $15\frac{1}{2}$ per cent greater than P_1.

4.3 Underground transmission cables

The grid and supergrid transmission lines are taken underground in urban areas and in some areas of outstanding natural beauty, e.g. Traeth Mawr in the Snowdonia National Park. The cost of taking the supergrid underground is so high, between 9 and 17 times the cost of an overhead line, that in most cases it is cheaper to take an overhead line on a longer route round a relatively small area of outstanding natural beauty. Cables are also less reliable by a factor of about 25. That is to say, the time for which a cable will be out of commission due to faults will be 25 times as long as an overhead line of the same length. This is because cables need repair more often and also take longer to repair.

Cable construction

All insulated electric cables consist essentially of three parts: (i) the conductor; (ii) the insulation; and (iii) the external protection or sheath. The conductor is usually made of copper or aluminium, both of which have high conductivities. Many types of insulation have been tried, but at the time of writing oil-impregnated paper tape is still the only one favoured for the supergrid cables. A power system cable insulation must have:

1. A high dielectric strength to withstand high operating and transient voltage stresses.
2. A low power factor to minimise the heat generated.
3. A low relative permittivity to minimise the charging current.
4. Flexibility to withstand bending during installation.

The full equivalent circuit of a short length of an a.c. cable is shown in Fig. 4.16 and is superficially similar to that of an overhead line. In this case, however, the shunt resistance may be thought of as

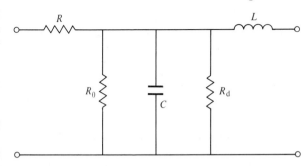

Fig. 4.16 Full equivalent circuit of a short length of cable.

two separate terms, R_0 the dielectric resistance and R_d representing the dielectric loss. The other parameters are L the series inductance, R the conductor resistance and C the shunt capacitance between the conductor and the sheath. Typical values of these parameters for a 1 km length of one phase of a 400 kV supergrid cable with a copper conductor having an area of 2 000 mm^2 are:

$$L = 0.4 \text{ mH} \qquad R = 9 \text{ m}\Omega \qquad R_0 > 3 \times 10^{10} \, \Omega$$
$$R_d = 3.5 \text{ M}\Omega \qquad C = 0.38 \, \mu\text{F}$$

At a load current of 1.9 kA the reactive power absorbed in L is 0.45 MVAr per km length per phase and the reactive power generated in C is 6.4 MVAr per km length per phase. The capacitance is much more significant and therefore, if the real power loss can be ignored, the cable can be represented, approximately, simply by a shunt capacitance as shown in Fig. 4.17 with a typical value of 0.4 μF per phase per km. Unlike the overhead line, this circuit is valid for any load current from zero to full load. Although it is convenient to represent the cable capacitance as a single lumped component, the capacitance is really distributed evenly over the whole length of the cable.

The current-carrying capacity of a particular cable is controlled essentially by the maximum conductor temperature at which it may

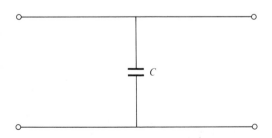

Fig. 4.17 Approximate equivalent circuit of a short cable.

33

4.3 Underground transmission cables

Table 4.3 Electrical characteristics of grid and supergrid cables

Line voltage (kV)	132	275	400
Conductor area (mm^2)	350	1 000	2 000
Rated current (A)	705	1 045	1 145
Apparent power (MVA)	160	500	800
Capacitance per phase, (μF/km)	0.399	0.375	0.381
Charging current (A/km)	9.56	18.7	27.6

be operated safely. Most transmission cables are buried underground and for these soil temperatures, soil thermal resistivity, depth of burial and, possibly, the heating effect of adjacent cables will all have a bearing on their current ratings. Typical values for cables with copper conductors and corrugated aluminium sheaths, buried 1 m deep with 150 mm between phases, are given in Table 4.3.

These ratings can be increased substantially with improved cooling, for example for a 2 000 mm^2 cable in air the rating is increased to 1.7 kA and with water cooling to 1.9 kA or more.

The high capacitance of cables leads to problems with large charging currents, or put another way, to large reactive power generation. The charging current necessitates a de-rating of long cables, and a critical length could be reached where the capacitance takes the full rated current. For the 400 kV cable in Table 4.3 this length is 41.5 km. In practice, cables of an appreciable length are divided into sections, and reactive power compensation is applied between sections by the addition of shunt inductors. For a short cable the inductors can just be added at each end. The compensation adds significantly to the cost of an a.c. cable installation, typically adding between 20 and 25 per cent to the cost. Reactive power compensation is difficult to apply to cables under the sea and long undersea cables usually carry direct current.

D.C. cables

D.C. cables offer a number of important advantages. They do not generate reactive power and so do not need reactive power compensation. They have no dielectric loss so the main loss is the I^2R loss in the conductor. Even this could be eliminated by using superconducting conductors made of, for example, niobium–tin or niobium–zirconium compounds, although at present it would not be economically viable due to the high cost of installing and running the cooling equipment. Another advantage of a d.c. cable link is that it can be buried in a much narrower trench than an a.c. cable system, and so is more suitable for urban areas. The narrower trench width is a consequence of the much lower heat dissipation from the d.c. cables and also only two cables may be required rather than at least three for an a.c. system. The C.E.G.B. has d.c. links from Kingsnorth to Beddington and Beddington to Willesden in London.

An interesting use of d.c. cables is to interconnect two a.c. systems which are not synchronised. The English Channel cable is an example which links the C.E.G.B. system at Lydd with the French system at Boulogne. The cable can carry 160 MW at 200 kV for 64 km. It allows the transfer of power to France during their daily peak demand and the transfer in the reverse direction during the daily peak demand in Britain. Fortunately the peaks do not occur at the same time. In principle this could provide a useful saving of generating plant and running cost, but the cable is a very weak link, carrying less than 1 per cent of the C.E.G.B. peak demand. The C.E.G.B. and Electricité de France have agreed to install a second link of 2 GW capacity.

One disadvantage of d.c. circuits is that it is very difficult, and therefore in most cases uneconomic, to provide circuit breakers to operate on high-voltage, high-current d.c. circuits. However, it is often possible to confine the switching to the a.c. part of the system. Another disadvantage of d.c. circuits is that they require rectifiers to change the a.c. to d.c. and inverters to change the d.c. back to a.c. These components add considerably to the cost of a d.c. link.

4.4 Switchgear

In a power system switchgear is required to:

1. Automatically isolate faulty components as rapidly as possible so that the remainder of the system can continue operating.
2. Allow equipment not required at a particular time to be taken out of service.
3. Isolate equipment for routine servicing or repair.
4. Prevent the spread of overvoltage surges. These are usually caused by lightning discharges on or near overhead lines.

There are three essentially different types of switchgear:

1. *Circuit breakers* which are switches designed to open, not only on full-load current, but also when carrying the much higher fault currents.
2. *Fuses* which are designed to open only on fault currents. They must be replaced before the circuit can be re-energised.
3. *Isolators* which are switches that can only be opened when the circuit is dead, although they can close onto a live circuit.

Modern circuit breakers are of three main types: (i) oil; (ii) air blast; and (iii) sulphur hexafluoride (SF_6). All circuit breakers consist in essence of a fixed contact and a moving contact. When closed, these are held together by a spring. When the breaker opens, the moving contact separates from the fixed, and draws out an arc. This arc must be interrupted and this is made easier in an a.c. system, by the fact that the arc current passes through zero twice each cycle. The detailed design of an oil breaker is often very complicated but the physical processes are straightforward. The heat of the arc breaks down (cracks) a small quantity of oil to form a large volume of gas, mostly hydrogen. The high pressure of this gas is used either literally to blow out the arc, or to force cold oil from a reservoir onto the arc, which is thus cooled and extinguished.

In the air-blast breaker, compressed air from a reservoir at a pressure of about 14 atmospheres is directed onto the arc at high velocities, thus extinguishing it. The air blast is usually directed along the axis of the electrodes, 'axial blast', and carries the arc through a hole in the fixed contact. Another type is the 'cross blast', in which the arc is forced onto splitter plates at the side. Arcs can be extinguished about 20 times more efficiently in sulphur hexafluoride as compared with air, but the gas is comparatively expensive and so such breakers must be equipped to recirculate the gas.

The rating of a three-phase circuit breaker is conventionally expressed by multiplying the maximum current it is designed to break, by the working voltage times $\sqrt{3}$, although of course, the maximum current occurs on fault conditions when the voltage usually drops considerably. A three-phase line requires a minimum of three breaker contact pairs, one pair for each phase. The factor $\sqrt{3}$ is introduced so that the quoted rating is the apparent power for the whole line and not just for one phase. High-voltage circuit breakers often have several pairs of contacts in series in each phase. The breaking capacity of the circuit breakers operated by the C.E.G.B. has risen progressively from 1.5 GVA on the early 132 kV grid system to 35 GVA on the present 400 kV supergrid. The rise is due partly to the increase in voltage but more especially to the increase in short-circuit current, as a consequence of more power stations being added to the system.

4.5 The power transformer

In general, one phase of a power transformer can be represented by a perfect transformer and four fixed components as shown in Fig. 4.18, where R accounts for the winding resistance (the copper loss), R_0 accounts for the core loss, X accounts for the leakage reactance and X_0 accounts for the magnetising current. On no-load R_0 and X_0 are the dominant parameters while on full-load R and X are more important. Usually X is larger than R, and if the power loss is not being calculated the transformer on load can be represented approximately by X and a perfect transformer, as shown in Fig. 4.19. It will be shown in the next section that it is possible also to eliminate

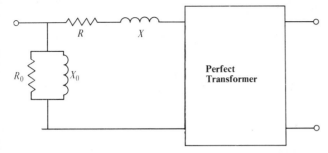

Fig. 4.18 Equivalent circuit for one phase of a power transformer.

the perfect transformer. A perfect transformer is an idealised concept of a transformer with the following properties:

1. The primary and secondary windings have no resistance, so there is no I^2R loss in either the primary or the secondary winding.
2. The permeability of the magnetic core is infinitely large so there is no leakage flux from the core and no magnetising current.
3. There are no losses in the core.

Thus there are no losses of any kind in a perfect transformer. If the primary winding has N_1 turns and the secondary winding has N_2 turns, then the transformation ratio, N, is given by:

$$N = \frac{N_2}{N_1}$$

Applying an alternating voltage V_1 across the primary winding of a perfect transformer results in an alternating voltage V_2 appearing across the secondary winding where:

$$V_2 = NV_1$$

If the current in the primary winding is I_1 then the current in the

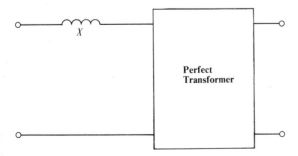

Fig. 4.19 Approximate equivalent circuit for one phase of a power transformer.

secondary winding, I_2, is given by:

$$I_2 = \frac{1}{N} I_1$$

Alternatively, and more simply, the perfect transformer may be thought of as a 'black box' which multiplies the voltage by N, divides the current by N and has no losses.

4.6 Per-unit values

When analysing power systems it is often found that the calculations can be simplified by using ratios to express the system quantities, rather than the quantities themselves. This idea is already familiar because efficiency and losses are often expressed as percentages.

A voltage V can be expressed in terms of per-unit (pu) by selecting a suitable base voltage V_B and determining the ratio:

$$V_{pu} = \frac{V}{V_B}$$

In general the per-unit value is

$$\frac{\text{the actual value of a quantity}}{\text{the base value of the same quantity}}$$

This equation applies to any electrical quantity, e.g. voltage, current, apparent power and impedance.

The base values of the various quantities may not be chosen at random, but must conform to the relations which normally hold between voltage, current, impedance, etc. Thus for a single-phase system:

$$S_B = V_B I_B, \qquad Z_B = \frac{V_B}{I_B} \quad \text{and therefore} \quad Z_B = \frac{V_B^2}{S_B}$$

For a three-phase system:

$$S_B = \sqrt{3} V_B I_B, \qquad I_B = \frac{S_B}{\sqrt{3} V_B}, \qquad Z_B = \frac{V_B}{\sqrt{3} I_B}$$

and again

$$Z_B = \frac{V_B^2}{S_B}$$

If this is done, the usual laws of electric circuit theory will also apply to per-unit quantities, i.e.

$$V_{pu} = I_{pu} Z_{pu}, \qquad P_{pu} = \sqrt{3} V_{pu} I_{pu} \cos \phi$$

It is usual to select first a base value for the apparent power which will apply throughout the system. Any convenient base may be chosen. The base voltage is selected next, and the base values of current and impedance are now fixed by the above relations. Note, however, that the base voltage is not the same in all parts of a system containing transformers.

The ratio of the base voltage on the secondary side to the base voltage on the primary side of a transformer must be equal to the transformation ratio.

This is most conveniently achieved by taking as base voltages the nominal transformer voltages. If this is done, and provided all work is done in per-unit quantities, the perfect transformer may be eliminated.

Example 4.1

A 20 MVA transformer with 11 kV primary and 66 kV secondary, has a reactance of 0.242 Ω referred to the primary. What is the per-unit reactance on the primary side? What is the per-unit reactance referred to the secondary?

1. Let $S_B = 20$ MVA and on the primary side $V_B = 11$ kV, then:

$$Z_B = \frac{V_B^2}{S_B} = \frac{11^2 \times 10^6}{20 \times 10^6} = 6.05 \,\Omega \quad \text{but} \quad X_B = Z_B$$

$$\therefore \ X_{pu} = \frac{X}{X_B} = \frac{0.242}{6.05} = 0.04 \text{ pu}$$

2. Transferring 0.242 Ω to the secondary side gives $X_2 = 0.242 \times N^2 \,\Omega$ where N is the transformation ratio. In this case $N = 6$.

$$\therefore \ X_2 = 0.242 \times 6^2 = 8.712 \,\Omega$$

On this side S_B is still 20 MVA but V_B is now 66 kV,

$$\therefore \quad Z_B = \frac{V_B^2}{S_B} = \frac{66^2 \times 10^6}{20 \times 10^6} = 217.8 \,\Omega \quad \text{but} \quad X_B = Z_B$$

$$\therefore \ X_{2pu} = \frac{8.712}{217.8} = 0.04 \text{ pu}$$

as before.

It is often necessary to convert per-unit reactances from one base to another. Suppose that the base apparent power is changed from an old value S_B to a new value S_B'. If X is a reactance, then on the old base, the per-unit value of this reactance, X_{pu}, is given by:

$$X_{pu} = \frac{X}{X_B}$$

or $\quad X_{pu} = \frac{XS_B}{V_B^2}$ $\qquad \ldots$ (i)

On the new base, the per-unit value of this same reactance, X'_{pu}, is given by:

$$X'_{pu} = \frac{XS'_B}{V_B^2} \qquad \ldots \text{(ii)}$$

Eliminating X/V_B^2 from (i) and (ii) gives:

$$\frac{X_{pu}}{S_B} = \frac{X'_{pu}}{S'_B}$$

or $\quad X'_{pu} = X_{pu}\dfrac{S'_B}{S_B}$ $\qquad \ldots$ (iii)

Expression (iii) gives the rule for converting a per-unit reactance from one base apparent power to a new base apparent power.

The per-unit value of the phase voltage at a point in a system will always be the same as the per-unit value of the line voltage at that point. This means that when working with per-unit quantities we do not have to be quite so careful to distinguish phase and line voltages.

To understand why the perfect transformer can be eliminated, when working in per-unit, consider the base voltages and impedances on each side of a perfect transformer. By taking base voltages proportional to the nominal transformer voltages, we ensure that the base voltage on the secondary side of each transformer is N times the base voltage on the primary side, where N is the transformation ratio. Because Z_B is proportional to V_B^2 it follows that the base impedance on the secondary side is N^2 times the base impedance on the primary side. However, the actual impedance referred to the secondary side is also N^2 times the actual impedance referred to the primary side. This means that an impedance will have the same per-unit value on each side of a transformer. In other words, transferring a per-unit impedance across a transformer does not change its value. So, provided all work is done in per-unit quantities, the perfect transformer may be eliminated.

4.7 Representation of a power system

Since, in most power systems, the three phases are balanced, it is enough in a diagram to show just one phase. It is usual also to omit

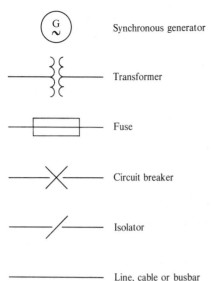

Synchronous generator

Transformer

Fuse

Circuit breaker

Isolator

Line, cable or busbar

Fig. 4.20 Symbols used to represent the components of a power system.

the neutral line, leaving what is known as a one-line diagram. The symbols used to represent the components on a one-line diagram of a power system are shown in Fig. 4.20.

Example 4.2.

Figure 4.21 represents a one-line diagram of part of a power system. Find the voltage of the supergrid busbar, V_{sg}.

First choose a base apparent power, $S_B = 100 \, \text{MVA}$. Choose the base voltages the same as the nominal transformer voltages, i.e. 275 kV, 132 kV and 66 kV. Next find the base impedance for the line, Z_B

$$Z_B = \frac{V_B^2}{S_B} = \frac{132^2 \times 10^6}{100 \times 10^6} = 174 \, \Omega$$

Now the per-unit reactance of the line can be found from:

$$X_{pu} = \frac{j3.48}{174} = j0.02 \, \text{pu}$$

For the supergrid transformer $X_{pu} = j0.1 \, \text{pu}$ (given). For the load transformer the per-unit reactance is given on a base of 50 MVA. This must be converted to a base of 100 MVA.

$$X_{pu} = j0.04 \times \frac{100}{50} = j0.08 \, \text{pu}$$

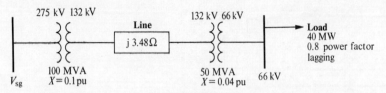

Fig. 4.21 One-line diagram of part of a power system used in example 4.2.

The base current at the load can be found from:

$$S_B = \sqrt{3}V_B I_B \quad \text{giving} \quad I_B = \frac{100 \times 10^6}{\sqrt{3} \times 66 \times 10^3} = 875 \text{ A}$$

The actual current at the load can be found from:

$$P = \sqrt{3}VI_L \cos\phi \quad \text{giving} \quad I_L = \frac{40 \times 10^6}{\sqrt{3} \times 66 \times 10^3 \times 0.8} = 437 \text{ A}$$

The per-unit value of the current $I_L = 437/875 = 0.5$ pu. The per-unit value of the load voltage, V_L, is 1.0 pu because the actual load voltage is the same as the base voltage.

The circuit can now be redrawn with per-unit values, as shown in Fig. 4.22. The three per-unit reactances add together to give a total reactance of j0.2 pu. The circuit then reduces to the simple equivalent circuit shown in Fig. 4.23.

The problem is now equivalent to the solution of a simple single-phase circuit.

Let the phase of the load voltage, V_L, be the reference phase. The load current, I_L, can then be expressed as a phasor in the form:

$$I_L = I_L \cos\phi - jI_L \sin\phi \text{ pu}$$

(The j term is negative because the load current is lagging.)

$$\therefore \quad I_L = 0.5 \times 0.8 - j0.5 \times 0.6 \text{ pu}$$

$$\therefore \quad I_L = 0.4 - j0.3 \text{ pu}$$

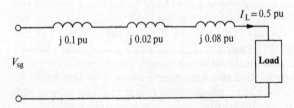

Fig. 4.22 Per-unit representation of example 4.2.

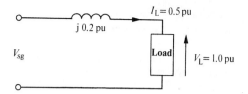

Fig. 4.23 Equivalent circuit of example 4.2.

The voltage drop across the inductor, V_i, is given by:

$V_i = I_L X$

$\therefore V_i = (0.4 - j0.3) \times j0.2$ pu

$\therefore V_i = 0.06 + j0.08$ pu

The voltage of the supergrid busbar, V_{sg}, is given by:

$V_{sg} = V_i + V_L$

$\therefore V_{sg} = 0.06 + j0.08 + 1.0 + j0$ pu

$\therefore V_{sg} = 1.06 + j0.08$ pu

The magnitude of V_{sg} is given by:

$|V_{sg}| = \sqrt{1.06^2 + 0.08^2}$ pu

$\therefore V_{sg} = 1.063$ pu

The base voltage at the supergrid busbar is 275 kV.

But $V_{pu} = \dfrac{V}{V_B}$ giving $V = V_{pu} \times V_B$

$\therefore V_{sg} = 1.063 \times 275$ kV

$\therefore V_{sg} = 292$ kV

Problems

1. A turbine generator supplying 290 MW to a power system has a terminal voltage of 22 kV and a generated e.m.f. of 16 kV per phase. If the synchronous reactance of the generator is 1.25 Ω per phase, calculate the torque angle. (36.5°)

2. If the excitation of the machine in problem 1 is increased to raise the e.m.f. to 20 kV per phase, how much reactive power will be generated assuming the torque angle remains unchanged?

(103 MVAr)

3. A 40 MVA gas-turbine generator is used to absorb reactive power from a power system, i.e. act as a synchronous compensator. The terminal voltage is 11 kV and the synchronous reactance per phase is 1.5 pu. What will be the generated e.m.f. per phase if the unit is absorbing 5 MVAr of reactive power? Assume the real power generated is negligible. (5.16 kV)

4. An overhead line 10 km long can be represented simply by a series inductive reactance of 2.7 Ω per phase. The line carries 1.8 GW with a sending-end voltage of 400 kV and a receiving-end voltage of 390 kV, what is the transmission angle? (1.8°)

5. A 50 Hz, single-phase line consists of two parallel conductors 30 cm apart. If each conductor has a diameter of 4 mm, calculate the reactance of a 500 m length of the line. (0.33 Ω)

6. A three-phase power line consists of three parallel conductors in the same horizontal plane. The two outer conductors are each 1 m from the centre conductor. If the conductor diameter is 6 mm, calculate the average inductance per phase of a 1 km length of the line. (1.3 mH)

7. A 1 kV, 50 Hz underground cable has a capacitance of 0.38 μF per km. How much reactive power will be generated in a 1.5 km length of the cable? (179 VAr)

8. A 400 kV, 50 Hz supergrid line is carried underground for 5 km. If the cable capacitance is 330 nF per phase per km, what is the total reactive power generated in the 5 km length?
(83 MVAr)

9. Calculate the charging current in each phase of the line in the previous question. If the apparent power rating of the line is 1.1 GVA, by what percentage must the maximum real power rating be reduced because of this charging current?
(120 A; 0.28 per cent)

10. Each phase of a three-phase circuit breaker is capable of withstanding a voltage of 76 kV and breaking a current of 10.9 kA. What is its rating? (2.5 GVA)

11. A circuit breaker for the 400 kV supergrid can break a 50.5 kA symmetrical three-phase fault current. What is the rating of the circuit breaker? (35 GVA)

12. In part of a single-phase system, take the base apparent power to be 48 kVA and the base voltage to be 240 V. Calculate: (i) the base current; (ii) the base impedance; (iii) 20 A expressed in per-unit; and (iv) 1.8 Ω expressed in per-unit.
(200 A; 1.2 Ω; 0.1 pu; 1.5 pu)

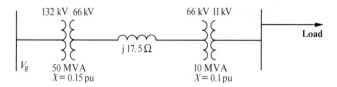

Fig. 4.24 One-line diagram of the circuit for problem 16.

13. A 50 Hz, 50 MVA transformer with a 132 kV primary and a 33 kV secondary has a reactance of 0.1 pu per phase. What is the reactance in ohms: (i) referred to the primary; (ii) referred to the secondary? (34.85 Ω; 2.178 Ω)

14. A 50 Hz, 500 MVA transformer with a 400 kV primary and a 275 kV secondary, has a total leakage reactance per phase referred to the primary of 38.4 Ω. Calculate: (i) the leakage reactance referred to the secondary; (ii) the per-unit reactance referred to the primary; (iii) the per-unit reactance referred to the secondary. (18.15 Ω; 0.12 pu; 0.12 pu)

15. A 20 MVA transformer has a reactance of 0.1 pu. What is its reactance on a base apparent power of 50 MVA? (0.25 pu)

16. Figure 4.24 represents a one-line diagram of part of a three-phase power system. Calculate the voltage of the grid busbar V_g, when the load busbar is at 11 kV and the load current is 1 kA at unity power factor. (138.76 kV)

Chapter 5
Power system control

5.1 Control of real power and frequency

The load, or demand, on a system is continuously changing. In England and Wales the most rapid change over 1 hour takes place between 7.00 a.m. and 8.00 a.m., and can be as large as 10 GW. At most times the total electrical output of the generators will not exactly balance the total load on the system plus losses. However, there must always be an exact energy balance, as demanded by the law of the conservation of energy. What happens is this. If the sum of the load plus losses of the system is greater than the total output of the generators, the extra energy comes from the kinetic energy of the machine rotors which slow down. If the load plus losses of the system is less than the output, the generators speed up. These changes of speed are reflected as changes in the frequency of the supply. On the British system a change of frequency is sensed by the turbine governors which adjust the opening of the steam valves to compensate, i.e. if the speed increases the valves start to close and if the speed decreases the valves start to open. The frequency is normally kept constant to 50 Hz ± 0.05 Hz. In practice speed control is complicated by the delay in the opening of the steam valves (0.2–0.3 s) and a further delay in the response of the low pressure turbines due to the large amount of steam trapped between the high-pressure turbines and the low-pressure turbines in the reheaters. It is a complicated problem in control engineering. It is much easier to see what happens in the case of a single generator feeding its own load in isolation.

Example 5.1

A 100 MW turbine generator is running at 3 000 rev/min, 50 Hz, on no-load. A 20 MW load is suddenly applied to the machine, and the governor starts to open the steam valve after 0.25 s. Calculate the frequency to which the generated voltage drops, before the steam flow increases in response to the increased load. The stored energy in the rotating parts is 400 MJ at 3 000 rev/min.

Before the steam valve opens the machine loses:

$$20 \times 10^6 \times 0.25 = 5 \times 10^6 \, \text{J} = 5 \, \text{MJ}$$

The stored energy left $= 400 - 5 = 395$ MJ. The kinetic energy of rotation is $\frac{1}{2} J\omega^2$ (J is the polar moment of inertia of the system), i.e. the kinetic energy is proportional to the frequency squared. Hence $400/395 = 50^2/f^2$ where f is the new frequency, giving $f = \sqrt{50^2 \times 395/400} = 49.69$ Hz.

5.2   Control of reactive power and voltage

As mentioned earlier there must always be a balance between the reactive power produced and the reactive power absorbed. What happens if there is a sudden increase in the reactive power demand without a corresponding increase in the reactive power produced? Consider a simple case of a voltage source feeding a load through a line, as shown in Fig. 5.1. The phasor diagram corresponding to this circuit is shown in Fig. 5.2 where ϕ is the phase angle of the load and δ is the transmission angle of the line. V_S and V_R are the source and load voltages respectively, of a single-phase system or equally they can be the phase voltages of a star-connected, three-phase system.

If δ is very small then the magnitude of the voltage difference between V_S and V_R, ΔV_P say, can be obtained from Fig. 5.2 by resolving the phasors in a horizontal direction which gives:

$$\Delta V_P = IR \cos \phi + IX \sin \phi \qquad \qquad \ldots \text{(i)}$$

But $I \cos \phi = P_R/V_R$ and $I \sin \phi = Q_R/V_R$, where P_R and Q_R are the real power and the reactive power consumed by one phase of

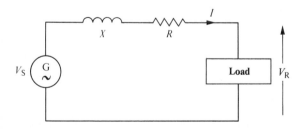

Fig. 5.1 Voltage source feeding a load through a line.

5.2   Control of reactive power and voltage

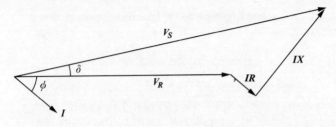

Fig. 5.2 Phasor diagram of a voltage source feeding a load through a line.

the load. Substituting in the expression (i) gives:

$$\Delta V_P = \frac{RP_R}{V_R} + \frac{XQ_R}{V_R}$$

$$\therefore \quad \Delta V_P = \frac{RP_R + XQ_R}{V_R} \qquad \qquad \dots \text{ (ii)}$$

For a three-phase system we conventionally work in terms of the total real power P, the total reactive power Q, the line voltage of the load V and the line voltage drop ΔV. The conversions are:

$$P = 3P_R, \qquad Q = 3Q_R, \qquad V = \sqrt{3}V_R, \qquad \Delta V = \sqrt{3}\Delta V_P$$

Substituting in the expression (ii) gives:

$$\Delta V = \frac{RP + XQ}{V} \qquad \qquad \dots \text{ (iii)}$$

Note that X is the magnitude of the reactance and not the reactance phasor.

If $X \gg R$, as it is for the supergrid overhead power lines, then expression (iii) may be simplified to:

$$\Delta V = \frac{XQ}{V} \qquad \qquad \dots \text{ (iv)}$$

This means that the voltage drop depends on the reactive power flow. If there is a sudden increase in the demand for reactive power by the load, this will increase ΔV and so cause a fall in the load voltage which in turn reduces the reactive power demand.

On the British system as a whole, a reduction of voltage of 1 per cent produces a 5 per cent reduction in the reactive power demand. (It also produces a 1.4 per cent drop in the real power demand.)

Example 5.2

A 15 km length of the 275 kV supergrid can be represented by a resistance of 0.51 Ω and an inductive reactance of 4.9 Ω per phase. The total load on the end of the line is 550 MW at a power factor of 0.9 lagging. Calculate the voltage drop along the line.

$$X = 4.9\,\Omega, \qquad R = 0.51\,\Omega, \qquad P = 550\,\text{MW}, \qquad \cos\phi = 0.9$$

$$\therefore \quad \phi = 25.8°$$

Now $S = P/\cos\phi$ and $Q = S\sin\phi$.

$$\therefore \quad S = \frac{550}{0.9} \quad \text{and} \quad Q = \frac{550}{0.9} \times \sin 25.8° = 266.4\,\text{MVAr}$$

Using the expression (iii) derived above:

$$\Delta V = \frac{RP + XQ}{V} = \frac{0.51 \times 500 + 4.9 \times 266.4}{275}\,\text{kV} = 5.8\,\text{kV}$$

Use of the above formula for ΔV is justified only if the transmission angle, δ, is very small. It is not too difficult to calculate an exact value of ΔV by multiplying the line current phasor by the line impedance. The calculation yields a value $\Delta V = 5.92\,\text{kV}$ and shows that the simple formula is in error by only 154 V which is probably less than the error introduced in estimating the line reactance. The small error in this example is a consequence of the very small value of the transmission angle, δ, which in this case is 1.9°. Larger values of δ would, of course, lead to larger errors in using the simple equation.

Example 5.3

A 5 km length of the 132 kV grid can be represented by a resistance of 0.8 Ω and an inductive reactance of 2.05 Ω per phase. The total load on the end of the line is 80 MW at a power factor of 0.8 lagging. Calculate the voltage drop along the line: (i) neglecting the resistance; (ii) including the resistance of the line.

$$X = 2.05\,\Omega, \qquad R = 0.8\,\Omega, \qquad P = 80\,\text{MW}, \qquad Q = 60\,\text{MVAr}$$

Using expression (iv) for ΔV gives:

$$\Delta V = \frac{XQ}{V} = \frac{2.05 \times 60}{132} = 0.93\,\text{kV} \quad \text{(neglecting the resistance)}$$

Using expression (iii) for ΔV gives:

$$\Delta V = \frac{RP + XQ}{V} = \frac{0.8 \times 80 + 2.05 \times 60}{132} = 1.42\,\text{kV} \quad \text{(including the resistance)}$$

Neglecting the resistance clearly leads to a large percentage error in

ΔV, but expressed in terms of the line voltage the error is only 485 V in 132 kV. At power factors closer to unity the percentage error in ΔV is even larger.

Again the validity of the calculation rests on δ being very small. In this example $\delta = 0.38°$.

Summary

Failure to keep up with the real power demand causes a drop in frequency.

Failure to keep up with the reactive power demand causes a drop in voltage.

5.3 Generation and absorption of reactive power in a power system

Large alternators can generate reactive power up to 50 per cent of their rated output but only absorb reactive power up to 15 per cent of their rated output when producing full load real power. Shunt capacitors are used to generate reactive power but they have the disadvantage that their reactive power production is proportional to V^2. Thus, just when they are needed most, to compensate for a shortage of reactive power which has caused a fall in the local voltage, their own output falls. Old steam plant which is needed only at times of peak demand can be used at other times to generate reactive power. This can be done with one boiler on about half load feeding steam to all the sets in a station. When generating reactive power in this way, the energy input is just that needed to overcome the losses. Old steam plant is often ideally situated in urban areas, close to where the reactive power is consumed. Machines known as synchronous compensators can either generate or absorb reactive power. Electrically they are similar to alternators but they are not coupled to a mechanical drive. They are in fact synchronous motors with automatic voltage regulators controlling their fields. They run continuously but only consume a small amount of real power to overcome their losses. If the system voltage falls, the regulator increases the field of the machine so that it generates more reactive power. If the system voltage rises, the regulator weakens the field and the compensator absorbs reactive power. Gas-turbine generators, when not needed to meet the real power demand, can often be declutched from their turbines and run as synchronous compensators.

All the components of a power system will absorb or generate reactive power. Some will do either, depending upon their mode of

50

operation. To summarise they are listed below:

Reactive power absorption	Reactive power generation
Reactive power absorption	*Reactive power generation*
Alternators under-excited.	Alternators over-excited.
Synchronous compensators under-excited.	Synchronous compensators over-excited.
Overhead lines on heavy load.	Overhead lines on light load.
Transformers.	Underground cables.
Inductors.	Capacitors.
A typical load.	

In practice, balancing the supply with the demand, for reactive power, is made difficult by: (i) the change from generating to absorbing in overhead lines as the load is increased; (ii) the importance of keeping large quantities of reactive power from being carried by the supergrid; and (iii) the change in the number and location of the generating sets which are needed to meet the real power demands at different times of the day. The reason why the supergrid should not carry large quantities of reactive power is as follows. The rating of an overhead line is fixed by its rated voltage and maximum current. Thus the maximum apparent power, S_{max}, is fixed. If a large quantity of reactive power is carried, the power factor, $\cos \phi$, will be significantly less than unity. Thus the maximum real power which is equal to $S_{max} \cos \phi$ will be significantly reduced. This is illustrated by example 5.4 below. Also, and probably more important, for a given real power transmitted, the losses are significantly increased due to the increased current. This is because the largest power loss in an overhead line occurs through heating of the conductors which is proportional to $I^2 R$. This effect is illustrated by example 5.5 below.

Example 5.4

Find the real power that can be carried by a 400 kV quad-conductor overhead line which is carrying 1 080 MVAr of reactive power.

From Table 4.1 a 400 kV quad-conductor line is rated at 1 800 MVA in normal weather.

$$\therefore\ S = \sqrt{3}\,VI = 1\ 800 \text{ MVA}$$

The reactive power, Q, is given by:

$$Q = \sqrt{3}\,VI \sin \phi = 1\ 080 \text{ MVAr}$$

$$\therefore\ \sin \phi = \frac{Q}{S} = \frac{1\ 080}{1\ 800} = 0.6$$

$$\therefore\ \cos \phi = 0.8$$

The real power, P, is given by:

$P = S \cos \phi$

$\therefore \ P = 1\,800 \times 0.8 = 1\,440 \ \text{MW}$

The line will now carry only 1 440 MW instead of a possible 1 800 MW. This is not an economical way to use the supergrid.

Example 5.5

Compare the power lost as heat in a 400 kV quad-conductor overhead line carrying 1 GW of real power only, with the same line carrying 1 GW of real power together with 750 MVAr of reactive power.

When the line is carrying 1 GW of real power only, the current, I_1, is given by:

$$I_1 = \frac{P}{\sqrt{3}\,V \cos \phi}$$

In this case $\cos \phi = 1$,

$$\therefore \ I_1 = \frac{10^9}{\sqrt{3} \times 400 \times 10^3} = 1\,443 \ \text{A}$$

The resistance of the line is $0.020 \ \Omega$ per km length (Table 4.2). The power lost in the line, P_1, is given by:

$P_1 = 3I_1^2R$ watts per kilometre (the 3 because there are three conductors)

$\therefore \ P_1 = 3 \times 1\,443^2 \times 0.020 \ \text{W per km}$

$\therefore \ P_1 = 125 \ \text{kW per km}$

Now consider the line carrying 750 MVAr of reactive power as well as the 1 GW of real power.
The current, I_2, is still given by:

$$I_2 = \frac{P}{\sqrt{3}\,V \cos \phi}$$

But now $\phi = \arctan \left(\dfrac{750}{1\,000} \right)$

$\therefore \ \cos \phi = 0.8$

$$\therefore \ I_2 = \frac{10^9}{\sqrt{3} \times 400 \times 10^3 \times 0.8} = 1\,804 \ \text{A}$$

The power lost in the line, P_2, is given by:

$P_2 = 3I_2^2R$ watts per kilometre

$\therefore \quad P_2 = 3 \times 1\,804^2 \times 0.020$ W per km

$\therefore \quad P_2 = 195$ kW per km

Note that P_2 is 56 per cent larger than P_1, i.e. the power lost in a line which is carrying much reactive power, is significantly larger.

Problems

1. A turbine generator is delivering 20 MW at 50 Hz to a local load: it is not connected to the grid. The load suddenly drops to 15 MW, and the turbine governor starts to close the steam valve after a delay of 0.5 s. The stored energy in the rotating parts is 80 MJ at 3 000 rev/min. What is the generated frequency at the end of the 0.5 s delay? (50.775 Hz)

2. A 10 km length of 400 kV, three-phase overhead line can be represented by an inductive reactance of 2.7 Ω per phase. The receiving-end busbars are at 400 kV when supplying a load of 1 GW at a power factor 0.8 lagging. What is the sending-end voltage? (405 kV)

3. A 50 Hz, 132 kV grid line is 5 km long. At the receiving end there is a load of 100 MVA. The line can be represented by a resistance of 0.16 Ω per phase per km and an inductance of 1.3 mH per phase per km. Calculate the voltage drop along the line if the load power factor is: (i) 0.8 lagging: (ii) 0.95 lagging, and (iii) 0.93 leading. (1.4 kV, 1.06 kV, 0.0 kV)

4. If in problem 2, a synchronous compensator were added to supply a current of −j1.51 kA to the receiving end busbars, what would the sending-end voltage be? Assume the load and the receiving-end busbar voltage are unchanged. (398 kV)

5. A three-phase, 50 Hz line which can be represented by an inductance of 1.25 mH per phase connects the sending-end busbars to 440 V load busbars. A load taking 15 kW at a power factor of 0.8 lagging is supplied from the load busbars and three capacitors in star, each 130 μF, are also connected to the load busbars. Calculate the sending-end busbar voltage. What fall in the sending-end busbar voltage would result in the load busbars falling to 415 V? Assume the load still takes 15 kW. (443 V, 24 V)

Chapter 6

Faults in a power system

6.1 Types of fault

The word 'fault' in the context of a power system means electrical breakdown, usually in the form of an arc, between phases of the system or from one or more phases to earth. Since faults cannot be avoided altogether, it is important to know how the system will react to a fault at any particular point.

Figure 6.1 shows the types of fault which can occur: here the three horizontal lines represent the three phases of a system. Type (i), breakdown from any one conductor to earth, is the common form of fault, but types (iii), breakdown from all three phases to earth, and (v), breakdown between all three phases, put the greatest perturbation on the system. These two types of fault are in fact equivalent, although they do not look it at first sight, also, being symmetrical, the calculation of fault current can be made in terms of one phase only. This type of fault is known as a symmetrical three-phase fault and since it is the most serious from the point of view of the stability of the system and also the easiest to calculate, we shall confine our attention to such faults.

On any system other than a very small system, the detailed calculation of the fault current is very difficult and usually unnecessary. The calculations can be made much easier if a number of simplifying assumptions are made. These are:

1. Each generator produces its nominal e.m.f. which remains unchanged by the fault.
2. All the generators are in phase with each other.
3. The reactance of each generator drops to about one-fifth of its steady-state value and stays constant during the fault. This reduced reactance is known as the transient reactance, is denoted by X' and is often given in fault calculation problems.
4. The load currents are ignored because they are in general much smaller than the fault current. In any case they are variable.
5. The fault forms a short-circuit of zero impedance.

54

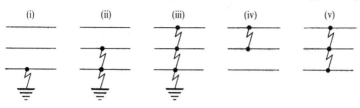

Fig. 6.1 Types of fault which can occur on a three-phase line.

It is conventional to quote fault apparent power in terms of the fault current and the normal system line voltage at the point of the fault. This follows the convention used for circuit-breaker ratings, but of course assumption (5) above implies that the voltage at the point of the fault is zero. The fault apparent power is also known as the fault level.

Fault calculations are best worked in terms of per-unit quantities.

6.2 Calculation of fault current and fault apparent power

Considering only one phase to neutral and looking into the system from the point of the fault, the Thévenin equivalent of the system is a voltage source in series with an impedance as shown in Fig. 6.2. Here V_T is the Thévenin equivalent *phase* voltage. Clearly the short-circuit current, I_{sc}, is given by:

$$I_{sc} = \frac{V_T}{Z} \qquad \qquad \ldots \text{ (i)}$$

It is more convenient to work in terms of per-unit quantities. Choose the nominal line voltages in the system as the base voltages. Choose any convenient base apparent power S_B. Then by definition:

$$S_B = \sqrt{3} V_B I_B \qquad \qquad \ldots \text{ (ii)}$$

and $\quad Z_{pu} = \dfrac{Z}{Z_B}$

$\therefore \; Z_{pu} = \dfrac{Z S_B}{V_B^2} \quad$ because $Z_B = \dfrac{V_B^2}{S_B} \quad$ (see section 4.6)

$\therefore \; Z = \dfrac{Z_{pu} V_B^2}{S_B}$

Substituting this expression for Z in equation (i) gives:

$$I_{sc} = \frac{V_T S_B}{Z_{pu} V_B^2}$$

6.2 Calculation of fault current and fault apparent power

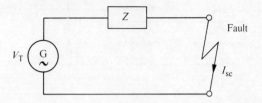

Fig. 6.2 Thévenin equivalent of one phase of a system with a fault.

Substituting for S_B from equation (ii) gives:

$$I_{sc} = \frac{V_T}{Z_{pu}V_B^2} \times \sqrt{3} V_B I_B$$

$$\therefore \quad I_{sc} = \frac{\sqrt{3} V_T I_B}{Z_{pu} V_B} \qquad \qquad \text{... (iii)}$$

Remember we have assumed that the load currents can be neglected, which is another way of saying there are no paths to earth in the system. With no paths to earth, the Thévenin equivalent phase voltage, V_T, is equal to the nominal generated phase voltage, V_P, referred to the point of the fault, i.e. $V_T = V_P$. But the nominal generated line voltage is our base voltage so

$$V_P = \frac{V_B}{\sqrt{3}} \quad \text{and} \quad \therefore \quad V_T = \frac{V_B}{\sqrt{3}}$$

Substituting for V_T in equation (iii) gives:

$$I_{sc} = \frac{I_B}{Z_{pu}} \qquad \qquad \text{... (iv)}$$

The definition of short-circuit apparent power is $\sqrt{3}$ times the nominal line voltage at the point of the fault multiplied by the short-circuit current.

To derive an expression for the short-circuit apparent power, S_{sc}, multiply each side of equation (iv) by $\sqrt{3} V_B$ giving:

$$\sqrt{3} V_B I_{sc} = \frac{\sqrt{3} V_B I_B}{Z_{pu}}$$

The left-hand side is, by definition, S_{sc} and the numerator on the right-hand side is S_B, therefore:

$$S_{sc} = \frac{S_B}{Z_{pu}}$$

If the resistances in the system can be neglected this expression

56

becomes:

$$S_{sc} = \frac{S_B}{X_{pu}}$$

and expression (iv) becomes:

$$I_{sc} = \frac{I_B}{X_{pu}}$$

Note that these expressions are valid only if we take the nominal line voltages in the system as our base voltages. We are not free to choose any base voltages.

Example 6.1

In the system shown in Fig. 6.3 a symmetrical three-phase short-circuit occurs on the 22 kV load busbars. Find the fault apparent power and the fault current.

First choose a base apparent power of 150 MVA. This is the largest of the given ratings, but any value may be chosen and the arithmetic can sometimes be simplified by choosing a value equal to the lowest common multiple of all the apparent power ratings given in the problem. The base voltages must be the nominal busbar voltages.

For the transmission line, the per-unit reactance is given by:

$$X_{pu} = \frac{X}{X_B} = \frac{X S_B}{V_B^2} = \frac{33 \times 150 \times 10^6}{132\,000^2} = 0.284 \text{ pu}$$

Convert the other reactances to a 150 MVA base using the

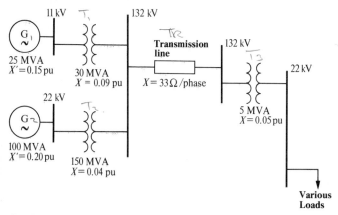

Fig. 6.3 One-line diagram of the circuit for example 6.1.

6.2 Calculation of fault current and fault apparent power

expression derived in section 4.6:

$$0.15 \times \frac{150}{25} = 0.9 \text{ pu} \qquad 0.09 \times \frac{150}{30} = 0.45 \text{ pu}$$

$$0.20 \times \frac{150}{100} = 0.3 \text{ pu} \qquad 0.05 \times \frac{150}{5} = 1.5 \text{ pu}$$

(Note that a per-unit value greater than unity, i.e. a percentage value greater than 100 per cent, does not imply that a mistake has been made. By using a suitable value of S_B any per-unit value can be obtained.)

The system can now be redrawn with all the reactances in per-unit to the same base, as shown in Fig. 6.4.

We can add the two generators in parallel. This is allowed because they are assumed to be in phase and generating the same per-unit voltage of unity. Now 1.35 pu in parallel with 0.34 pu gives 0.272 pu. The three reactances in series give $0.272 + 0.284 + 1.5 = 2.056$ pu. The circuit becomes that shown in Fig. 6.5 which is in fact the Thévenin equivalent of one phase of the system, looked at from the point of the fault. Using the expression for S_{sc} derived in section 6.2 we have:

$$S_{sc} = \frac{S_B}{X_{pu}} = \frac{150 \times 10^6}{2.056} = 73 \text{ MVA}$$

Using the expression for I_{sc} derived in section 6.2 we have:

$$I_{sc} = \frac{I_B}{X_{pu}} = \frac{S_B}{\sqrt{3} V_B X_{pu}} = \frac{150 \times 10^6}{\sqrt{3} \times 22\,000 \times 2.056} = 1.9 \text{ kA}$$

Sometimes fault calculations can be made without reference to the whole system. This is done by considering only that part of the system close to the fault, together with the Thévenin equivalent of the rest of the system feeding power in at some point, P, say. This point will usually be a connection to the grid or the supergrid. The short-circuit apparent power which the grid can supply at the point

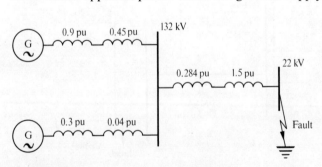

Fig. 6.4 Per-unit representation of example 6.1.

58

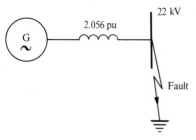

Fig. 6.5 Thévenin equivalent of one phase of example 6.1.

P may be quoted instead of the Thévenin equivalent circuit. This is called the short-circuit rating of the grid. It can be changed easily to a per-unit Thévenin equivalent circuit as shown in the following example:

Example 6.2

In the system shown in Fig. 6.6 there is a grid feed of 500 MVA short-circuit rating onto the 132 kV busbars at the point P. A symmetrical short-circuit occurs on the 22 kV busbars. Find the fault apparent power and the fault current.

The base voltage at P must be 132 kV. Choose a base apparent power of 100 MVA: this is an arbitrary choice.

The next step is to replace the grid feed by its per-unit Thévenin equivalent. To do this we use the expression $S_{sc} = S_B/X_{pu}$ which was derived earlier.

$$\therefore\ X_{pu} = \frac{S_B}{S_{sc}} = \frac{100 \times 10^6}{500 \times 10^6} = 0.2\ \text{pu}$$

The grid feed can therefore be thought of as a voltage source of 1.0 pu behind a reactance of 0.2 pu.

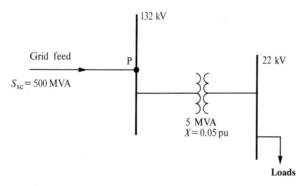

Fig. 6.6 One-line diagram of the circuit for example 6.2.

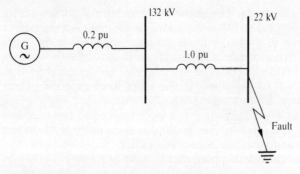

Fig. 6.7 Per-unit representation of example 6.2.

Next convert the 5 MVA transformer to a 100 MVA base:

$$X_{pu} = 0.05 \times \frac{100}{5} = 1.0 \text{ pu}$$

The diagram can now be redrawn with all the reactances in per-unit to a base of 100 MVA, as shown in Fig. 6.7. We can now find the short-circuit apparent power from:

$$S_{sc} = \frac{S_B}{X_{pu}} = \frac{100}{1.2} \text{ MVA} = 83 \text{ MVA}$$

The fault current, as before, is given by:

$$I_{sc} = \frac{I_B}{X_{pu}} = \frac{S_B}{\sqrt{3} V_B X_{pu}} = \frac{100 \times 10^6}{\sqrt{3} \times 22\,000 \times 1.2} = 2.2 \text{ kA}$$

6.3 System protection

The generators, transformers, cables and other components of an electric power system are very expensive items and it is necessary to protect them from damage due to excessive currents and excessive voltages occurring at any point in the system. If a component develops a fault, it is important that the faulty component be isolated from the rest of the system as rapidly as possible, to preserve the stability of the rest of the system. Another requirement is the maintenance, as far as possible, of an electrical supply to all consumers. There is one exception, however, which is mentioned later. A transmission network is usually arranged so that if a fault occurs on a component, that component can be isolated by opening (tripping) circuit breakers on each side of it and so isolating the faulty component from the rest of the system. In a closely interconnected system the rest of the system can then go on working normally or at least under conditions near to normal. If the faulty component is a generator, other generators must make up the power deficiency as soon as possible. If the faulty component is an overhead line, or a transformer feeding an overhead line, then other lines will carry extra current. The system must be designed so that this extra current does not result in the other lines exceeding their maximum capacity. If alternative lines *were* overloaded, the protection system might react as if these too were faulty and isolate them from the rest of the system. This could put even more load on the remaining lines and result in these being tripped out successively. This is known as cascade tripping and is most likely to occur when the power system is heavily loaded due to very cold weather. Cascade tripping can lead to power failures over a large area as has happened more than once in the north-east of the United States. On 9 November 1965, seven states including the city of New York and also Ontario, Canada, were affected and about 30 million people were without power, some for as long as $13\frac{1}{2}$ hours.

Because of the need to isolate faulty components as rapidly as possible, automatic fault detection and protection systems are employed. These can isolate a fault in less than 150 ms, which includes the time for the protection circuit to detect the fault as well as the time for the circuit breakers to open. The protection system on a large power system is complex, but the principle is easy to understand by considering a simple arrangement. The simplest way of protecting a power system is to divide it up into a large number of sections or zones. One zone could be a length of overhead line. Circuit breakers are installed at each end of the line and the current flowing in each phase of the line is monitored by current transformers at each end. A current transformer is very small in power system terms, and the secondary current under normal conditions is typically 1 A. The primary, which is one phase of the overhead line, may be simply passed through the core on which the secondary is wound. The secondary will then be a toroidal winding and the primary effectively a single turn. With some current transformers the secondary side must always be loaded when the primary current is flowing or the transformer may be damaged by the very high secondary voltage. The secondary current in the current transformer is a measure of the current flowing in the section of overhead line where the transformer is situated. The current entering the section is compared with the current leaving the section, in a differential circuit. If the difference is large, due to a fault in this section of the line, the difference current trips a relay which in turn trips the circuit breakers at each end of the line. The section of line containing the fault is thus isolated from the rest of the system. In a similar way the line, or any other component, can be protected from excessive voltages by using a capacitive voltage divider to monitor the phase voltages.

6.3 System protection

After a fault has been detected and a section of line isolated, it is important to bring the section back into service quickly. To do this it is necessary to reclose the circuit breakers soon after the fault has been cleared. If the fault is due to a mechanical failure, for example, a tower brought down by the combined effect of ice and gale-force winds, it will not be possible to clear the fault for several days. However, one of the most common causes of faults on overhead transmission lines is lightning and such faults can be cleared and the circuit breakers reclosed in less than 1 s. In some power systems high-speed reclosing relays are used to automatically reclose the circuit breakers about half a second after they have tripped. If the fault is still present they trip again. When a fault persists after a reclosure, or in some systems two reclosures, the circuit breakers remain open. In other power systems, for example the C.E.G.B. system, the circuit breakers will normally be reclosed automatically after a delay of 10 to 20 s. This allows time for checks to be made on the system conditions. The checks are necessary because there are situations where reclosing the circuit breakers could result in the system becoming unstable.

An indication of the success of a closely interconnected transmission system is that less than 2 per cent of the faults on the British supergrid result in a loss of supply to consumers.

Each generator in a system will have its own circuit breaker which can be opened either manually or automatically if a fault develops on the generator. The generator is then said to be 'lost' from the system. Faults on generators or their associated circuits can have serious consequences, particularly when a large generator delivering full power is suddenly lost. In a small system, or a larger system which is lightly loaded, there will be a serious imbalance between the power generated and the power demand, after a large generator has been lost from the system. There may be sufficient 'spinning reserve' (see section 7.3) to cope with the imbalance but some systems use automatic load-shedding relays. This facility relies on having one or more customers to whom electricity is supplied on an interruptable basis. The supply contracts for these customers specify a maximum duration and number of interruptions per day, per week and per year. In return these customers receive their electricity at a lower cost than ordinary customers. Interruptable contracts are useful to an electricity company only if the customer normally uses a large quantity of electricity on a 24 hours per day basis. An aluminium smelter may well be supplied on this basis. In a power system with pumped storage, the pumping load can also be automatically interrupted. The supply is interrupted by tripping the load circuit breakers which are activated by frequency-sensitive relays. These relays continuously monitor the system frequency and if it falls below say 49.7 Hz, on a 50 Hz system, the first customer will be disconnected. A further fall in frequency may disconnect another customer. This gives a few minutes, during which gas-turbine generators can be started or hydro-electric plant brought into operation. The system frequency will then rise and the circuit breakers will automatically reclose to restore the supply to the interrupted customers.

Problems

1. Three 11 kV, 100 MVA generators are connected to common busbars. Each is connected via a 100 MVA inductor and an identical circuit breaker. The inductors have reactances of 0.15 pu, 0.20 pu and 0.30 pu. If the generators each have a transient reactance of 0.25 pu, what is the minimum circuit-breaker rating to protect the generators against a fault on the common busbars?   (250 MVA)

2. A symmetrical three-phase short-circuit occurs on the 22 kV busbars of the circuit shown as a one-line diagram in Fig. 6.8. Calculate the fault current and the fault apparent power.
                                                        (1.9 kA, 72 MVA)

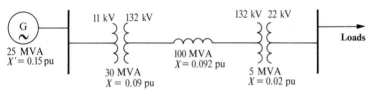

Fig. 6.8 One-line diagram of the circuit for problem 2.

3. A symmetrical three-phase fault occurs on the 11 kV busbars of the circuit shown in Fig. 6.9. Calculate the fault apparent power and the fault current.   (353 MVA, 18.5 kA)

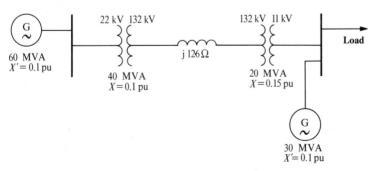

Fig. 6.9 One-line diagram of the circuit for problem 3.

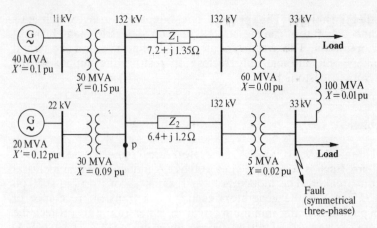

Fig. 6.10 One-line diagram of the circuit for problems 4, 5, 6 and 7.

4. Figure 6.10 represents a one-line diagram of a power system. A three-phase symmetrical fault occurs on the 33 kV busbars as shown. Calculate the fault level, the fault current and the line voltage at the point P, under the fault condition, but neglect the resistance of each of the line impedances Z_1 and Z_2.

(210 MVA, 3.7 kA, 37 kV)

5. Referring again to the previous question, is it possible to limit the fault current to 3.1 kA by increasing the reactance of the 100 MVA inductor? If so, to what value must it be raised? (Yes, 0.3 pu)

6. Referring again to the circuit in Fig. 6.10, calculate the fault level and fault current, taking the resistances of the lines into account. Does the inclusion of these resistances make a significant difference to the answers?

(210 MVA, 3.7 kV
No, the calculated fault level and fault current are
reduced by about 0.2%)

7. Suppose the system shown in Fig. 6.10 was modified by the addition of a grid feed of 500 MVA short-circuit rating onto the 132 kV busbars at the point P. A symmetrical short-circuit occurs on the 33 kV busbars as shown. Calculate the fault apparent power and the fault current. (384 MVA, 6.7 kA)

Chapter 7
Energy supplies

7.1 Power stations

There are five sources of energy which together account for nearly all the world's electricity. They are coal, oil, natural gas, hydro-electric power and nuclear energy. Coal, oil and nuclear plants use the steam cycle to turn heat into electrical energy, in the following way. The steam power station uses very pure water in a closed cycle. First it is heated in the boilers to produce steam at high pressure and high temperature, typically 150 atmospheres and 550°C in a modern station. This high-pressure steam drives the turbines which in turn drive the electric generators, to which they are directly coupled. The maximum amount of energy will be transferred from the steam to the turbines only if the latter are allowed to exhaust at a very low pressure, ideally a vacuum. This can be achieved by condensing the outlet steam into water. The water is then pumped back into the boilers and the cycle begins again. At the condensing stage a large quantity of heat has to be extracted from the system. This heat is removed in the condenser which is a form of heat exchanger. A much larger quantity of cold impure water enters one side of the condenser and leaves as warm water, having extracted enough heat from the exhaust steam to condense it back into water. At no point must the two water systems mix. At a coastal site the warmed impure water is simply returned to the sea at a point a short distance away. A 2 GW station needs about 60 tonnes of sea water each second. This is no problem on the coast, but inland very few sites could supply so much water all the year round. The alternative is to recirculate the impure water. Cooling towers are used to cool the impure water so that it can be returned to the condensers, the same water being cycled continuously. A cooling tower is the familiar concrete structure like a very broad chimney and acts in a similar way, in that it induces a natural draught. A large volume of air is drawn in round the base and leaves through the open top. The warm, impure water is sprayed into the interior of the tower from a large number of fine jets, and as it falls it is cooled by the rising air, finally being collected in a pond under the tower. The cooling tower is really a second heat exchanger where the heat in the impure water is passed to the atmospheric air; but unlike the first heat exchanger, the two fluids are allowed to come into contact and as a consequence some of the water is lost by evaporation. However, this is only about 1 per cent of the water which would be lost if no attempt were made to recycle the impure water. The amount lost can usually be supplied by a local river. Evaporation would eventually lead to an unacceptable build-up of impurities, and to counter this some extra water is extracted from the river while an equal quantity of the old water is returned to the river. The amount of this purge water required is about the same as that needed to make up for evaporation. The cooling towers are never able to reduce the impure water temperature right down to the ambient air temperature, so that the efficiency of the condenser and hence the efficiency of the whole station is reduced slightly compared with a coastal site. The construction of the cooling towers also increases the capital cost of building the power station. The need for cooling water is an important factor in the choice of sites for coal, oil and nuclear plants. A site which is suitable for a power station using one type of fuel is not necessarily suitable for a station using another fuel. Each may therefore, be considered separately.

Coal-fired power stations

Early coal-burning stations were built near the load they supplied. Some of the municipal stations are still to be seen within large towns and cities, but these are small by today's standards. More modern stations have been built at the edge of urban areas or further away in rural situations. A station of 2 GW output, consumes about 5 million tonnes of coal in a year. In Britain where most power station coal is carried by rail, this represents an average of about 13 trains a day each carrying 1 000 tonnes. This means that large coal-fired stations need a rail link unless the station is built right at the pit head. The latter has been done in a number of cases and the coal is carried directly by conveyer from the mine to the power station. It is economically attractive to build the power stations at, or close to, the coal mines because, using the supergrid, it is cheaper to move the electricity than the coal. This fact has led to a concentration of large coal-fired power stations over the coalfields, e.g. in the Trent Valley in England. The electricity from these stations is then moved, perhaps 100 km or more, to the load centre. This is known as the 'bulk transmission' of power. A coal-burning power station of 2 GW needs a fairly large site, because it will usually have to accommodate the following: a rail siding, preferably in the form of a loop, to avoid uncoupling the locomotive and so speed the turn-round; a fuel storage area where the coal can be stockpiled during the summer months as an insurance against shortages of supply during the winter; cooling towers; a supergrid substation and in some cases an ash disposal area. The main power station buildings occupy a small proportion of the whole site. The site should be on, or fairly near, an existing branch of the supergrid if possible. Lastly, consideration has to be given to access during construction as alternator stators and supergrid transformers are very heavy and boiler shells are very large. Clearly, proximity to a wide main road would be an advantage.

Oil-fired power stations

Power station oil can be divided into crude oil which is oil as it comes from the well, and residual oil which remains when the more valuable fractions have been extracted in the oil refinery. The cost of moving oil by pipeline is less than that of moving coal by rail, but even so stations burning crude oil are often sited near deep-water berths suitable for unloading medium-sized tankers. Stations burning residual oil need to be sited near to the refinery which supplies them. This is because residual oil is very viscous and can only be moved through pipelines economically if it is kept warm.

Nuclear power stations

In contrast to coal and oil the cost of transporting nuclear fuel is negligible because of the very small amount used. A 1 GW station needs about $4\frac{1}{2}$ tonnes of uranium each week. This compares very favourably with the 50 000 tonnes of fuel which would be burnt each week in a comparable coal-fired power station. Present nuclear stations use rather more cooling water than comparable coal-fired or oil-fired plants due to their lower efficiency. All nuclear stations in Britain with one exception, are situated on the coast and use sea water for cooling. The exception is Trawsfynydd in North Wales which uses a large lake for cooling. This is visually much more acceptable than cooling towers, particularly as this power station is in the Snowdonia National Park, an area of outstanding natural beauty. For safety reasons, early nuclear power stations in Britain were built in remote, thinly populated areas. More recently, as confidence in their safety has grown, sites nearer to large urban areas have been chosen.

Hydro-electric power stations

Hydro-electric power stations must be sited where the head of water is available, and as this is often in mountainous areas, they may need long transmission lines to carry the power to the nearest load centre or link up with the grid. All hydro-electric schemes depend on two fundamental factors: a flow of water and a difference in level or head. The necessary head may be obtained between a lake and a nearby valley, or by building a small dam in a river which diverts the flow through the power station, or by building a high dam across a valley to create an artificial lake. With a high head of 300 m or more, considerable velocity can be imparted to the water and this is used to drive a Pelton Wheel turbine. This is in essence a wheel with cups, or buckets as they are called, on the perimeter. The jet of water is directed into the buckets and the wheel turns in air driving the generator. The Pelton Wheel is an impulse turbine. For low heads a reaction turbine is used. This is rather like a multi-bladed propeller inside a tube through which the water flows. It is driven partly by the pressure of the water and partly by the velocity. All types of water turbines turn slowly and so if the generator, which is directly coupled to the turbine, is to generate at 50 or 60 Hz, it must have many poles. A typical speed is 500 rev/min, necessitating an alternator with 12 poles.

In many ways hydro-electric power stations provide the ideal way of generating electricity. They require no fuel, produce no atmospheric pollution either chemical or thermal, produce no waste products, are cheap to run, require little maintenance, can be started up very quickly (less than 1 minute) and have a long life of at least 50 years. Unfortunately, there are not many suitable sites in Britain, and most of these have already been developed. About 90 per cent of Britain's hydro-electric energy is generated in Scotland: most of it by the North of Scotland Hydro-Electric Board. The largest station is Loch Sloy 130 MW. The hydro generation represents about 2 per cent of Britain's total electricity production. The C.E.G.B. has some small plants in Wales, e.g. Rheidol (53 MW) in Central Wales, and Maentwrog (24 MW) in Snowdonia. Some other countries are more fortunate. Norway, for example generates more than 95 per cent of its electricity requirements in hydro stations, and the largest power stations in the world are hydro-electric. The Russians have built a 6 GW station at Krasnoyarsk on the Yenisey river in Siberia, and a much larger station to be built on the river Paraná on the border between Brazil and Paraguay is in the planning stage. This would have an ultimate output of 12.6 GW.

Gas-turbine generators

Power station gas-turbine generators are essentially aircraft engines coupled to generators. In spite of their name, gas turbines normally burn a light fuel oil known as gas oil, which is similar to paraffin, and this must be highly refined to exclude impurities such as vanadium and sulphur which would otherwise shorten the life of the turbine blades. There are no special site requirements. No cooling water is required and no large fuel store, so that a small site is quite adequate. Some plants are built in urban areas, sometimes on the sites of disused coal-fired stations, where they are ideally situated for the generation of reactive power when not being used to meet the peak load demand. The 110 MW station at Lister Drive in Liverpool is an example of such a station. Other gas-turbine generators are installed on the same sites as some large modern oil- and coal-burning stations where they take up comparatively little extra space. The 2 GW coal-fired power station at Fiddler's Ferry on the river Mersey, also houses a 70 MW gas-turbine plant.

Gas-turbine generators are, compared with steam plant, cheap to install and also have the advantage that they can be started up in a few minutes. Their disadvantage is that they are expensive to run, partly due to a lower efficiency than steam plant, and partly due to the high fuel cost which results from the need to run on highly refined fuel. In fact, gas-turbine engines can be adapted to run on a wide range of fuels from natural gas to coal dust, but the problem is one of maintenance, and life of the turbine blades.

Diesel engines

Large internal combustion engines similar to marine diesel engines can also be used as prime movers to generate electricity. From a power system point of view their properties are similar to gas-turbine generators except that they run much more slowly and burn their fuel at a much higher efficiency, comparable with that of a large steam plant. The fuel is, however, 35 to 40 per cent more expensive than the oil for an oil-burning steam plant. Diesel engines are the first choice to supply electricity to small isolated communities when it is not economic to connect them to the grid. The Shetland Islands, off the north coast of Scotland are, at the time of writing (1978), supplied entirely by diesel engine generators. Ten engines are installed in a station in Lerwick which together can generate 36 MW. It is likely that a gas-turbine station will be built soon, probably at Sullum Voe, to cope with the increased demand associated with the North Sea oil development. Plans have also been made to build a second diesel power station at Lerwick.

Geothermal power

The heat in the interior of the earth can, in principle be used to produce steam and hence, drive steam-turbine generators. This has only been done on a small scale up to now, and in each case where the steam occurs naturally as a geyser or hot springs. The earliest plant was built at Larderello near Pisa in northern Italy, and now has an output of 370 MW. There is a 160 MW station at Wairakei in New Zealand and also a number of power plants at The Geysers in northern California, USA, in Japan and in Iceland.

Tidal power

The idea of using the tidal flow of water to generate power in the Severn Estuary in England, has been discussed for many years. The world's first major tidal power station was built in the Rance Estuary in St Malo Bay, France. Here the tidal range is large, being an average of 10.9 m, and a dam was built across the mouth of the estuary so that as the tide rises, water flows through the turbines to fill the estuary and generate power. The turbines are reversible so that as the tide falls the water flowing out of the estuary also generates power. Because of the low and variable head, the efficiency is very low, but this is not so important when there is no fuel cost. The actual source of energy is the angular momentum of the earth. Generating electricity at Rance slows down the rate of rotation of the earth by an extremely small amount.

A much larger tidal power plant is, at the time of writing (1978), being constructed in the Bay of Fundy on the Atlantic coast between Canada and the United States. This scheme will be capable of generating 2 GW.

The disadvantage of tidal schemes, from the power system point of view, is that the times of high and low tide change every day, so that sometimes the plant will be generating at times of peak load, but on other days it will be idle. It is possible by sacrificing some of the available energy, to adjust the water levels so that the plant can generate at the time of peak demand every day. Alternatively, tidal schemes could be built so that they include a pumped storage element (see section 7.4). The main objection to tidal schemes is the high cost of the civil engineering works necessary.

Natural gas

Any steam power station burning coal or oil could fairly easily be converted to burn natural gas, and two power stations in England are capable of burning either coal or gas. Such stations must, of course, be situated near a large gas main. However, it is generally felt in this country that natural gas is too high a quality fuel and too valuable as an industrial feed stock and home heating fuel, to be used in power stations. The point is that gas burnt to produce electricity which might then be used for home heating, would produce heat at about 33 per cent efficiency, whereas the same gas burnt in a domestic boiler would produce heat at up to 80 per cent efficiency. If very large quantities of natural gas were available it would, no doubt, be used much more for electricity generation.

7.2 Fuel for electricity generation

The significant sources of energy for electricity generation fall into three distinct groups. Firstly, fossil fuels: coal, oil and natural gas; secondly, solar energy: at present only hydro-electric power; and thirdly, nuclear energy from uranium or plutonium. The percentage contribution of each fuel to the total amount of fuel used by a particular system, depends primarily on the type of plant installed, and to a much smaller extent on the current fuel costs. Hydro stations have zero fuel cost and nuclear stations have a low fuel cost so the only real scope for switching fuel in response to prices is between the fossil fuels. Table 7.1 shows the contributions of different fuels to the electricity generated in England and Wales. It shows the shift from oil to coal in response to the larger price increases in oil during the years in question. The contribution from nuclear energy is near to the maximum possible for the system. Hydro power does not appear in the table because it contributes only about 0.2 per cent to the installed capacity.

By far the largest running cost item of an electricity undertaking which produces a large proportion of its energy from burning fossil fuel is the cost of the fuel itself. It is unfortunate, therefore, that this fuel can only be converted into electricity with an efficiency of 30 to 35 per cent. Put another way, this means that about two-thirds of the fuel bought is wasted as heat thrown away. Most of this heat goes into the condenser cooling water and is subsequently dissipated in the atmosphere, in a river or in the sea. In some countries, notably Denmark and Sweden, large areas of towns are heated from the cooling water of local power stations. This system is known as district heating and large, thermally insulated, water mains are laid under the streets. The condenser cooling water leaves the power station at a higher temperature than normal for a conventional power station. This results in a lower efficiency of the steam cycle, and so a lower efficiency of generation. The important factor, however, is the efficiency measured as useful output (heat and electricity) divided by the total fuel energy input. This can be as high as 80 per cent. One objection to these schemes, which is often raised, is that the homes, shops and offices do not need heating in the summer and the power station must, therefore, be provided with

Table 7.1 Fuel consumption in millions of tonnes of coal or coal equivalent by the C.E.G.B. in recent years.

	1974–5	1975–6	1976–7	1977–8	1978–9
Coal	64.8 (64%)	67.5 (70%)	70.6 (72.5%)	70.3 (70%)	75.5 (72.5%)
Fuel oil	23.6 (23%)	16.9 (17%)	14.1 (14.5%)	16.3 (16%)	17.6 (17%)
Natural gas	3.6 (3.5%)	3.8 (4%)	2.0 (2%)	2.1 (2%)	0.5 (0.5%)
Nuclear fuel	9.5 (9.5%)	8.7 (9%)	10.7 (11%)	11.7 (12%)	10.6 (10%)

an alternative way of rejecting its waste heat. A more satisfactory solution is to shut down the plant during the summer. The electricity production is then lost for these months, but as the summer demand is much less than the winter demand (see the next section), other stations in the system can easily cope. A small scheme of this type was built at Battersea in London many years ago.

The most attractive opportunity to install a district heating scheme occurs when a new town in built in a rural area. The town and power station can then be planned together and the heating mains installed before the roads and buildings are constructed.

7.3 Base and peak loads

The fact that electricity cannot be stored in worthwhile quantities has a profound effect on power system management. It means, of course, that enough electricity must be generated at all times to meet the demand. A gas system has considerable storage in the mains and other pipework, but there is no storage of energy in the transmission and distribution networks of an electric power system to meet unexpected increases in the demand. The variations in demand are, therefore, very important to the power engineer. These variations can be studied on a daily, weekly and annual basis. Figure 7.1 shows the load (or demand) against time curve for the C.E.G.B. system in 1977–8 for a typical winter day and a typical summer day. There is a marked difference between night and day. Demand is low during the night when most people are asleep, and rises rapidly between 6.00 a.m. and 9.00 a.m. In the summer this rise represents nearly a doubling of the load in 3 hours, and about 12 GW of plant must be brought into operation to meet the demand. In winter, as well as the morning rise, there is an evening peak between 5.00 p.m. and 6.00 p.m. This is produced by people returning home from work and switching on lights, heaters and cookers. This evening peak presents a problem to the power engineer because it must be met by plant which is required to generate for only 2 or 3 hours each day and then only in the winter.

The average demand over a year, divided by the maximum demand which occurs during that year, is called the system load factor: typical values are 50 to 60 per cent. From the point of view of economic operation, the system load factor should be as high as possible, which explains why electricity is often cheaper during the night. This, it is hoped, will encourage the use of storage heaters which will improve the system load factor by consuming more electricity during the night.

In some hot countries the summer demand is greater than the winter. This comes about where the winter is not cold enough to

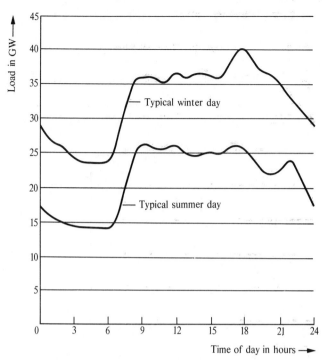

Fig. 7.1 Load (or demand) at different times of day for the C.E.G.B. system in 1977–78 showing a typical winter day and a typical summer day.

need much electric heating, but the summer is so hot that extensive use is made of air conditioning plant.

An alternative way of expressing the daily load is to plot each load value against the total length of time during each day that the particular load value is exceeded. This is known as the load-duration curve. Figure 7.2 shows the load-duration curve corresponding to a typical winter day, derived from the curve in Fig. 7.1. The axes of these curves look very similar, but note that the horizontal axis of the load-time curve is 'time of day', whereas the horizontal axis of the load-duration curve is 'duration in hours'. This curve may be divided into three parts as follows:

1. The base load which must be met continuously, i.e. for 24 hours each day.
2. The intermediate load which lies between (1) and (3).
3. The peak load which is demanded for, say, 10 per cent of the time, i.e. 2 to 3 hours.

For economic reasons the base load should be supplied by the most efficient stations in terms of running cost. These will be first

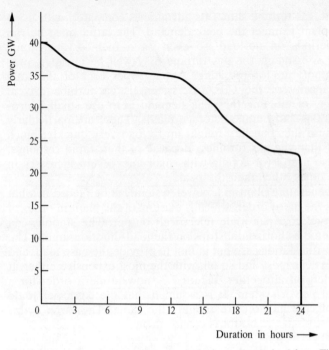

Fig. 7.2 Load-duration curve for a typical winter day derived from Fig. 7.1.

the nuclear, and then the most modern coal- and oil-burning stations. They will be manned with a three-shift work force for 24 hours each day. In a system where there are large hydro-electric plants and plenty of water available, these may also supply some or all of the base load. Small hydro-electric plants, because of their flexibility, are better used to supply the peak demands.

The intermediate load can be met by the older coal- and oil-burning stations, and inevitably will be idle for some part of each day. The boilers must be kept alight and generally will produce enough steam to keep the turbine generators in synchronism with the rest of the system.

The peak load can be met in a number of ways. The most attractive at present is to use gas-turbine generators. These are expensive to run because of the higher cost of their fuel (highly refined gas oil) and low efficiency, but this is offset by their low capital cost. If only used for a short time each day, their high fuel cost is not important, but if they were called upon to generate for longer times, they would be uneconomic compared with steam plant. The break-even point occurs when they are run for about 10 per cent of the day. They also have the advantage over steam plant, that they can be started up and put on load in about 2 minutes. This

74

is where the gas turbine shows its advantages compared with using old steam plant to meet the peak demand. The latter must be run for long periods on no-load, so even on a fuel cost per joule (electrical) assessment, the gas turbine may well be cheaper, provided it is not run for too long. About 3 per cent of the total installed capacity of the C.E.G.B. system is gas-turbine driven. Another way of meeting the peak demand is to use small hydro-electric stations and pumped storage plants. These are particularly useful because they can be brought up to load very quickly: much faster even than the gas turbines. Because of their rapid response, they are also useful for coping with small unexpected increases in demand at times other than the peak.

All the generating plant in a power system can be placed in what is known as the merit order, which is a listing of the plant in order of increasing fuel cost per joule (electrical) output. The stations can then be plotted as horizontal strips on the load-duration graph. The cheapest-to-run stations are put in first to provide the base load, and then the next cheapest and so on, with the most expensive either at the top or left off altogether. Figure 7.3 shows a merit order for a hypothetical power system. It is assumed that the costs per joule (thermal) of coal and oil are roughly the same. The large hydro stations must be at the bottom because their fuel cost is zero. Next come the nuclear stations with their low fuel cost, then the most modern coal- and oil-burning stations with their relatively high efficiencies (33 to 36%), followed by the older coal- and oil-fired stations and above them the old, small coal-fired stations. Above these are the small hydro plants which are clearly out of place on a strict fuel cost basis, but are placed here because of their flexibility. The top of the curve extending horizontally to a maximum of about 2 hours is supplied by the gas-turbine generators. This merit order, shown in Fig. 7.3, is somewhat over-simplified in that it ignores transmission costs and some other factors, but it gives the general picture of how the stations in a power system would be used. Pumped storage schemes can alter the shape of the load-duration curve and will be considered in the next section.

At any particular time, some of the generators which are synchronised to the system will be running on only part load so that they can respond almost instantly (less than 1 s) to any sudden increase in demand. This is called spinning reserve by power engineers. The engineers controlling a power system try to predict a day or two in advance what the demand is likely to be at every minute of the day. To do this they study past demand records, weather forecasts and even television programme schedules. It is not the electricity consumed by the television sets themselves which is significant, but rather the habits of the people watching. At the end of a popular programme, many people stop watching and move into another room where they may turn on lights, electric fires and plug

7.3 Base and peak loads

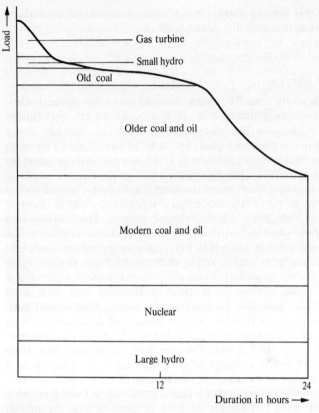

Fig. 7.3 Merit order of a hypothetical power system.

in electric kettles. Normally these actions would have a negligible effect on the power system, but if they are made almost simultaneously by perhaps a million people the effect is substantial. At such times the demand can rise by up to 2 GW within a few minutes in Britain.

The cost per joule (electrical) of supplying a small increase in the demand, at any given time, is called the incremental cost. It is equal to a weighted average of the cost of generation at those stations on part load at that particular time. These, of course, are the only stations which can supply the extra energy. At first sight the merit order would suggest that at times of low demand the incremental cost would be low. This is not necessarily true. Even at times of low demand such as a summer Sunday afternoon, it may be necessary to start up gas-turbine generators to cope with a sudden increase in demand which was not predicted, or a sudden increase which is expected to last for only a few minutes. It is true to say that the incremental cost is high at the time of peak demand, particularly in the winter when most of the plant is in use.

7.4 Energy storage

Clearly, any electric power system is not being used in the best way, from a fuel cost point of view, if efficient coal and oil-fired power stations are running at reduced power for part of the day, while gas-turbine generators which are expensive to run, have to be used at other times. If some means were available so that energy could be stored at times of low demand, in such a way that it could be released later at times of peak demand, then there would be an overall saving of fuel. Whether there would also be an overall financial saving depends on the capital cost of constructing the storage plant. In practice, no storage system operates without losses and so the efficiency of the plant must also be taken into account. Storage will show a financial saving if the cost of the storage cycle per joule of electricity stored is less than the difference in incremental cost per joule between base load generation and peak load generation. The difference in incremental cost per joule will suddenly become much larger than it is at present in Britain, when there is more than enough nuclear plant to supply the base load.

Electricity itself can be stored in secondary batteries, and while these are quite efficient their high capital cost, coupled with a relatively short life, makes them uneconomic.

The hydro-electric pumped storage scheme is the only system of storing energy on a large scale at present available to the power system engineer. In its simplest form the scheme consists of a low-level reservoir and a high-level reservoir close by. When storing energy, power is drawn from the grid to drive a synchronous motor which is coupled to a hydraulic pump. This pumps water from the lower reservoir through a pipeline to the upper reservoir. In the generating mode, water flows from the upper reservoir down the pipeline and through a turbine coupled to a generator, to produce electric power in just the same way as an ordinary hydro-electric power station. It is usual to make the same machine function both as a synchronous motor and an alternator, and in some installations the pump and turbine are also the same machine which is simply reversed to change mode.

Pumped hydro-electric storage schemes require rather special geological conditions. There must be a large difference in level over as short a horizontal distance as possible, and the rock must be such that it will retain the water, particularly in the upper reservoir. Clearly, they can only be built in mountainous regions and the lower reservoir is usually an existing lake, though some schemes dispense with the lower reservoir and pump their water from, and discharge their water to, a river. The upper reservoir might be an existing lake which may need enlarging or it might be entirely artificial. In the latter case a dam will have to be constructed high up on the mountain. It is an advantage if the lower reservoir is much larger than the upper one, so that the lower water level does not change too much. Large changes in level lead to an unsightly shoreline devoid of vegetation. The advantages of pumped storage are as follows: a very long lifetime, perhaps 70 years; a low running cost; a high efficiency, typically 75 per cent; and a short start-up time (less than 1 minute). The disadvantages are: a long lead time of 5 to 10 years; a high capital cost; and because the schemes are usually built far from load centres, high transmission costs. There may also be objections at the planning stage from environmental preservationists because, in Britain at least, the mountainous areas where such schemes could be built are also areas of outstanding natural beauty. However, several of the schemes already built have turned out to be tourist attractions in themselves.

The C.E.G.B. has a pumped storage plant at Ffestiniog in North Wales with an output of 360 MW and a storage capacity of 4.63 TJ, which is equivalent to full power for $3\frac{1}{2}$ hours. Full power can be brought up in under 1 minute. The head of water is 300 m and the same electrical machines serve as alternators and motors. This scheme was completed in 1963 and was the first pumped storage scheme in Britain.

The first pumped storage scheme in Scotland which was built on Ben Cruachan, has an output power of 400 MW. The scheme took advantage of a large existing lake, Loch Awe, as its lower reservoir. The upper reservoir, 350 m above, was formed by building a dam across the mouth of a natural corrie high up on the slopes of Ben Cruachan. The storage capacity is 30 TJ, equivalent to full power for 21 hours. The reason for the large storage capacity is that the original idea was to work the plant on a weekly cycle, generating each day, pumping back rather less each night and then making up the difference by pumping for longer on Sunday. However, the plant is now used in a different way as explained later. The power station is deep inside the mountain, being at its lowest point 36 m below the level of Loch Awe. It houses four reversible Francis pump/turbines which are coupled to motor/alternators: that is to say, the same machine acts as either a pump or a turbine, and this is coupled to an electrical machine which can be used as a synchronous motor or an alternator. Loch Awe is so large, about 40 km^2, that pumping and generating have little effect on its water level. Even pumping for 21 hours would only lower Loch Awe by 20 cm.

Another pumped storage scheme in Scotland at Foyers, uses the even larger Loch Ness as the lower reservoir. It has an output of 300 MW, storage of 20 TJ, equivalent to full power for nearly 19 hours and a 175 m head of water.

A much larger scheme is under construction at Dinorwic near Llanberis in North Wales, which will have a rated output of 1.5 GW and a maximum output of 1.88 GW. The storage capacity will be 27 TJ which is equivalent to rated output for 5 hours.

There are three essentially different ways in which a pumped storage scheme can be used as part of the overall running of a power system. The first and original way was to work on a daily cycle, generating for several hours during times of peak demand, and pumping during the early hours of the morning for long enough to refill the upper reservoir. Used in this way the load-duration curve is smoothed out as shown in Fig. 7.4, with a consequent saving in running costs. The second way of operating is to switch from pumping to generating and from generating to pumping many times each day to balance the rest of the system against small changes in the demand. The Cruachan and Foyers plants are operated in this way and in 1976 made an average of 45 changes of mode each day.

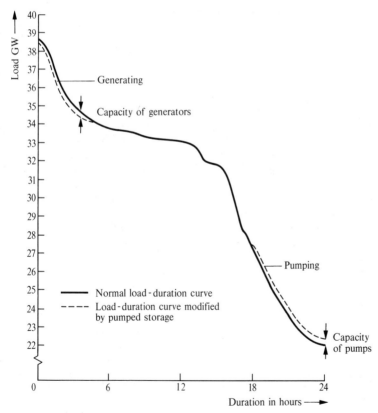

Fig. 7.4 Effect of pumped storage on the load-duration curve.

The third way of operating a pumped storage plant is to use it as a stand-by. The Dinorwic scheme was planned with this in mind and is designed so that it can be held available for immediate reserve generation for most of the day. In this mode the turbines will be kept running at zero output by passing just enough water to overcome the losses and maintain synchronism with the grid. In this way the output could be raised to 1.32 GW in 10 s which will cover the sudden loss of two 660 MW steam-turbine generators. Alternatively, the turbines could be kept running in compressed air, to hold back the water, using power from the grid at a lower operating cost. In this mode, the output could be raised in about 14 s.

Ultimately the amount of pumped hydro storage is limited by the number of suitable sites, so other forms of energy storage are being investigated. Chemical batteries have already been mentioned. What the power system engineer needs is a new type of secondary cell which is cheap and long-lasting. Electrical energy could be stored in capacitors. Storage densities of 3.6 MJ per litre are possible with thin glass-film dielectrics so a cube of 10 m sides would store 3.6 TJ, but storage life would be short due to leakage and the energy would be very difficult to control. Energy can be stored in a rotating flywheel. A wheel of 4 m diameter, weighing say, 100 tonnes, at 3 500 rev/min would store about 36 GJ for short periods at a capital cost comparable with pumped storage. The efficiency would depend on frictional and windage losses and the length of time for which the energy was stored. Magnetic fields can be used to store energy by maintaining large currents in super-conducting loops, but this system is likely to be very expensive. Energy storage in the form of heated liquids or small solid particles is possible, but the maximum efficiency is governed by the theoretical Carnot efficiency $(T_{max} - T_{min})/T_{max}$, and would be hopelessly low. The same is true for any storage cycle depending on a heat engine, for example the electrolysis of water followed by burning the hydrogen in a gas turbine.

At present the most promising new system is the storage of compressed air which could be used at times of peak demand to improve the efficiency of gas turbines by a factor of $2\frac{1}{2}$ times. This is because in a normal gas turbine 60 per cent of the fuel consumed is used to compress the air which is injected into the combustion chambers. A large volume would be needed, probably an underground cavern. A disused salt mine would be ideal. In such a system, electric compressors would be run at times of low demand to force air into the cavern. At peak demand times, the compressed air would be ducted into the front of a gas-turbine generator whose compressor could be declutched. The gas turbine could then be run in the normal way, but burning much less fuel for the same electrical output.

Figure 7.5 shows a compressed air storage scheme in its simplest

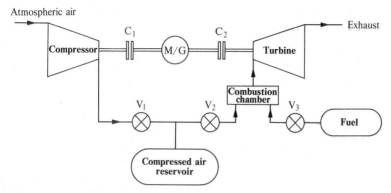

Fig. 7.5 Compressed air storage scheme.

form. To store air the clutch C_1 is engaged, the clutch C_2 is disengaged, the valve V_1 is open and the valve V_2 is closed. The motor/generator, M/G, is run as a synchronous motor, and using electricity from the grid it drives the compressor to charge the air reservoir with compressed atmospheric air. In the generating mode C_1 is disengaged, C_2 engaged, V_1 closed and V_2 open. Fuel and compressed air are fed to the combustion chamber, and the turbine runs like an ordinary gas-turbine engine but without a compressor. The turbine drives the motor/generator as a generator and this feeds electrical energy to the grid.

A compressed air scheme is, at the time of writing, (1978) being constructed at Huntorf in Germany.

7.5   Future developments

Experiments and design studies are being carried out to develop new ways of generating electricity. These fall broadly into three groups. Firstly, work associated with existing coal- and oil-burning power stations where efforts are being made to utilise the inherent thermodynamic efficiency of the very high flame temperatures of burning oil or pulverised coal. The flame temperature is clearly much higher than the steam temperature, but the thermodynamic efficiency of a conventional station depends on the steam temperature not the flame temperature. Generators have been constructed to convert some of the energy in the flame, which is a moving ionised gas, directly into electricity. These are known as magnetohydrodynamic generators.

Secondly, work is being done to try to convert solar energy into electricity. This is a wide subject which is covered extensively elsewhere. Listing some of the studies gives: windmills, wave power generators, silicon photocells, solar furnaces using mirrors and biological conversion systems.

Thirdly, we have what is sometimes called the nuclear alternative. Most nuclear power stations use uranium as a fuel. Natural uranium consists of two isotopes, uranium-235 and uranium-238 ($^{235}_{92}U$ and $^{238}_{92}U$) where the number 235 or 238 is the mass number, i.e. the total number of nucleons (protons and neutrons) in each nucleus, and 92 is the atomic number of uranium, i.e. the number of protons in each nucleus. Only the uranium-235 atoms can undergo fission in a thermal nuclear reactor, so only the uranium-235 constituent of the fuel elements produces the energy. Unfortunately, natural uranium contains only 0.7 per cent of uranium-235, so more than 99 per cent of the uranium which is mined and refined is waste material. In one respect it is almost like using coal with a 99 per cent ash content! However, there is a way in which the latent energy in the uranium-238 can be released. The process is indirect and involves a reactor known as a breeder reactor. Before explaining how this works, let us consider the ordinary natural uranium reactor in some detail.

When a uranium-235 atom undergoes induced fission the process can be described by the equation:

$$^{235}_{92}U + n \rightarrow {}^{236}_{92}U \rightarrow X + Y + (2 \text{ or } 3)n + \text{energy}$$

where n is a neutron and X and Y are fission products, typically elements with mass numbers near 95 and 140. The neutrons released have a high energy, they are 'fast' neutrons and must be slowed down to thermal energy before they can induce fission in another uranium-235 nucleus. The slowing down is done in the moderator which is placed between the fuel rods. In a natural uranium reactor the moderator is either graphite or heavy water (deuterium oxide). These materials slow down the neutrons without absorbing them significantly. Of the two or three neutrons released, one is needed to sustain the chain reaction while the remainder are absorbed elsewhere in the reactor. Some are absorbed in the fuel element canning material, some in the fission product nuclei, some in the control rods, some in the biological shield and some in the uranium-238. It is these last that are of interest. The process can be described by:

$$^{238}_{92}U + n \rightarrow {}^{239}_{92}U \xrightarrow{\beta} {}^{239}_{93}Np \xrightarrow{\beta} {}^{239}_{94}Pu$$

This means that a uranium-238 atom absorbs a neutron and becomes another isotope of uranium, uranium-239. This is radioactive and undergoes β (electron) emission with a 23.5 minute half-life, changing into neptunium-239. This in turn is also radioactive and decays by β emission, with a half-life of 2.35 days, into plutonium-239. Plutonium-239 is a nuclear fuel with properties similar to uranium-235 in that it will undergo fission in a nuclear reactor to produce energy. Thus some uranium-238 is converted into fuel in a natural uranium reactor.

The processes occurring in the breeder reactor are just those described above, except that the geometry is rearranged to enhance the production of plutonium. The nuclear fuel in the core of a breeder reactor is plutonium-239 and the core is very small compared with a gas-cooled thermal reactor. There is no moderator, and fission is induced by fast neutrons. Hence these reactors are sometimes called fast reactors. The core is surrounded by a blanket of uranium-238 to absorb as many neutrons as possible and thus produce or 'breed' plutonium. With careful design it is possible to breed more plutonium in the blanket than is consumed in the core. Because of the small core size, the power density is very high. This makes the design of the cooling system very critical. The United Kingdom Atomic Energy Authority has a breeder reactor at Dounreay on the north cost of Scotland. This is cooled by liquid sodium, and though primarily experimental, does deliver some power to the supergrid.

Breeder reactors can, at least in principle, utilise most of the available uranium and they can do even more. They can be designed to turn thorium, which does not undergo fission, into uranium-235 which is another fissile isotope of uranium. The process can be described by:

$$^{232}_{90}\text{Th} + \text{n} \rightarrow {}^{233}_{90}\text{Th} \xrightarrow{\beta} {}^{233}_{91}\text{Pa} \xrightarrow{\beta} {}^{233}_{92}\text{U}$$

The thorium atom after absorbing a neutron becomes the radioactive isotope thorium-233. This undergoes β emission with a half-life of 22 minutes, changing into protactinium-233. This in turn decays by β emission, with a half-life of 27 days, becoming uranium-233.

There are a number of major objections to the nuclear alternative. The two most serious of these are the risk of an accident to a reactor, releasing highly radioactive material into the atmosphere, and the problem of disposing of the radioactive fission products, some of which will remain significantly active for thousands of years. It is possible that future research will discover a way of de-activating the fission products, but there are no indications at present that a breakthrough is near.

A much more attractive nuclear energy approach to power generation lies in the use of nuclear fusion. This is the process which releases the enormous energy of the hydrogen bomb. Much research is being directed to the harnessing of fusion energy. One most promising reaction involves the fusion of two deuterium (heavy hydrogen) nuclei to form either helium or the even heavier isotope of hydrogen, tritium. The reactions are:

$$^2_1H + ^2_1H \rightarrow ^3_1H + p + 0.64\,pJ \text{ of energy}$$

or $\quad ^2_1H + ^2_1H \rightarrow ^3_2He + n + 0.51\,pJ$ of energy

where p is a proton.

There are three very important advantages which these fusion processes have over the fission of uranium or plutonium, as a source of energy for electricity generation. Firstly, there is an almost inexhaustible supply of deuterium in the sea. Secondly, there is no large accumulation of radioactive material in the power station, which might be released in the event of an accident. Thirdly, the only radioactive by-product is tritium which could easily be dealt with and might perhaps be used in the even more energetic reaction:

$$^2_1H + ^3_1H \rightarrow ^4_2He + n + 2.8\,pJ \text{ of energy}$$

It may well be that one or more of these three reactions will supply much of man's energy requirements in the twenty-first century. It is also possible that the major energy source will be the sun and that micro-organisms or plants, specially developed by the techniques of genetic engineering, will convert sunlight, water and atmospheric carbon dioxide into alcohol or methane, or perhaps hydrogen.

Index

Index